NAVIGATING THE INSURANCE MAZE

THE THERAPIST'S COMPLETE GUIDE TO WORKING WITH INSURANCE – AND WHETHER YOU SHOULD

FIFTH EDITION

By Barbara Griswold, LMFT

Paper Street Press
San Jose, California
www.theInsuranceMaze.com

Navigating the Insurance Maze: The Therapist's Complete Guide to Working with Insurance – And Whether You Should (Fifth Edition)
By Barbara Griswold

© April 2014, Fifth Edition by Barbara Griswold
Fourth Edition, 2013
Third Edition, 2011
Second Edition, 2008
First Edition, 2006

Published by Paper Street Press
San Jose, CA

Printed in the United States of America
www.theInsuranceMaze.com

This manual is intended to provide information to assist psychotherapists in different situations related to working with private insurance plans. It is not intended to address every situation that could potentially arise, and is not a substitute for independent legal, financial, or clinical advice or consultation. This manual attempts to give a general overview of private insurance plans. Some plans will not fit the descriptions herein. It is not intended as a manual for dealing with state or federal government plans such as Medicare or Medicaid. Use of this manual does not substitute for reading individual provider or member contracts, or contacting the insurance company for information on a specific plan or member's benefits. Be aware that laws, regulations, and technical standards vary with time and according to situational factors including the psychotherapist's license, state, and type and place of service. Thus, the reader should verify references or information contained herein.

ISBN: 978-0-9840027-2-6

*To my patient and selfless husband, Doug,
my amazing daughter, Maria,
my always-encouraging mom and dad,
who have supported me in everything I've ever done.*

How lucky am I?

Acknowledgments

ഇ ൙

This book would not have been possible without Barbara Grover, LMFT.
Many of the concepts in the book were developed with Barbara
as we prepared for presentations on this topic.

For their thoughtful feedback and copy-editing of the first edition, I thank
Yvonne Blockie, LMFT; Richard Ferry, LMFT, Marianne Corradi; and Karl Kahler.

And for the generous contributions of their advice, time, and talents, I thank:
Susan Frager, LCSW, of Psych Administrative Partners, my billing advice guru,
David Jensen J.D. and Michael Griffin, J.D., LCSW, Staff Attorneys at the California
Association of Marriage and Family Therapists, and
James Barrios at BR Printers, who patiently shepherded me through each edition of this
book.

Most of all, I thank all of you with whom I have had the pleasure to correspond, consult,
or meet at my workshops. I learn so much from you when you share your insurance
stories, struggles and successes. You remind me daily how much I have to learn, and keep
me humble.

Table of Contents

Introduction

೮ ೮

"A successful therapy practice is one where you don't need to take insurance."

This comment sums up how many therapists feel about working with insurance. We often see accepting insurance as equivalent to selling your soul to the devil, a sign of failure, or in the same way struggling actors see waiting tables: a way to earn income while making a name for ourselves.

I felt this way in 1990, when I became licensed as a Marriage and Family Therapist and joined my first insurance provider networks. I wanted referrals, and figured I could always resign when my practice was full. Now, 24 years later, I am a provider for more than 15 insurance networks. While I long ago reached my goal of a self-sustaining practice, I only resigned from three networks along the way. Hopefully this book will explain why.

As I talk to colleagues and workshop attendees on the subject of insurance, it has become clear that while we make our living in the health field, many of us are in the dark about basic facts about health insurance and reimbursement. Which begs the question: Why is this topic -- which has such a significant effect on our practice and even the therapeutic relationship -- left out of the training of most mental health professionals?

With or without this information, many therapists have made up their minds <u>not</u> to participate. In fact, a 2010 survey by the California Association of Marriage and Family Therapists showed that approximately 49 percent of their members had chosen not to affiliate with managed care provider networks[1]. Many clinicians have understandably been influenced by managed care horror stories. Fearing the compromise of confidentiality, loss of clinical control, micromanagement, increased paperwork, and discounted fees, many have chosen not to work with insurance. And those of us who do participate may feel we are stumbling along in the dark, making too many costly mistakes, as we navigate the ethical, clinical, and administrative issues that come up as we put insurance into our practices.

This lack of a dialogue on the myths and realities of insurance is what led me to write this book. The goal of this manual is <u>not</u> to persuade you to accept insurance. It isn't right for everyone. On some days, I'm not even sure it was right for me. My aim is to give practical information you didn't get in graduate school. Armed with facts instead of fears, I hope you'll be able to decide whether working with insurance is a wise idea for your practice. After all, this is one of the most important business decisions you will make as a therapist. But I see this as an area no therapist can avoid. We all have clients who seek insurance reimbursement, so it is important that we understand how insurance works, and what we need to do to help them seek reimbursement. What we <u>don't</u> know <u>can</u> hurt us – and our clients. And knowledge is power -- right?

I wrote this book because I am passionate about making the work we do accessible to people of all socio-economic backgrounds. Like you, I got into this profession to help others – not just the wealthy. Accepting insurance is one way to help clients from all walks of life to afford what we do. Also, there is something wrong when clients -- who have often paid hefty insurance premiums -- can't use their insurance coverage to see the therapist of their choice.

Please keep in mind the book's limitations. First, while I will make many generalizations, remember that each insurance plan's policies may differ. Second, the book focuses only on working with private insurance. While many of the concepts are useful for working with any third party coverage, the book does not cover the specific details of working with government plans such as Medicare, MediCal, Medicaid, or Victim Witness.

Writing and re-writing this manual (this is the fifth edition), leading workshops, and consulting with other therapists has been a humbling process: I continually learn how much I <u>don't</u> know. With any luck, after you are finished reading you will know what it has taken me 24 years to learn.

Barbara Griswold, LMFT

1

Why Take Insurance?

✲ ✲

As you traveled the long (it may have seemed unending) path toward licensure, perhaps you visualized your future psychotherapy practice. Maybe you dreamed of opening your own office. Of setting your own schedule. Of making a difference. Of having your own loyal and adoring clients. Most likely, you dreamed of a practice where each client paid your full fee out of pocket.

You probably didn't spend much time visualizing the business aspects of your future practice. Your training likely concentrated on the clinical, the theoretical, the legal and ethical sides of the field, but you probably never took a course on how to start, market, and maintain a small business. You may not even like to think of what you do as a business.

And that is why your visualization probably didn't include whether you'd take insurance. Perhaps you also heard stories from others that discouraged you from accepting insurance. The discounts. The paperwork. The limitations of coverage. The phone calls to check benefits and unsnarl claims problems. The need to discuss treatment decisions on occasion with case managers.

So Why Consider Accepting Insurance?

▶ **Private-pay is no longer the norm.** Therapists continue to want to focus on developing a private-pay-only practice, despite the fact that the number of clients who pay out-of-pocket is surprisingly small. According to a 2010 government study, private insurance was the most frequently used source of payment for health visits, with only 14.2 percent of these expenses paid out of pocket.[2] And in a 2006 *Psychotherapy Finances* survey, the average clinician reported that private-pay accounted for just 26 percent of their private practice income, a decrease from 44 percent just six years earlier.[3]

▶ **The Affordable Care Act (the ACA, also known as "healthcare reform") means that millions more Americans will have (or soon have) new or improved coverage for mental health care.** It may be harder to convince clients not to use their insurance, and to pay out of pocket for this care (for more on the ACA, see Page 36).

► **Insurance can be a great referral source.** When you become a provider for an insurance plan or employee assistance program, you may be contacted by clients who were given your name by their plan, which can help fill empty therapy slots. I get several calls each day from potential new clients who want to see someone on their plan. Due to my insurance participation my practice is always full, with a waiting list. Now, this is not everyone's experience -- as they say, "your mileage may vary."

► **It may reduce your need for marketing and advertising.** The insurance plan will give out the name of participating providers to plan members who call asking for referrals, and list these names on the insurance company website. If you hate advertising yourself, this is a nice benefit. You could think of your discounted rate as a prepaid marketing fee. "If you choose to let the insurance companies do the marketing, you will have more time to do therapy," says Casey Truffo, of The International Therapist Leadership Institute.[4] "Think of them as your sales staff. They work for you. You have basically hired them to do your marketing."

► **Insurance enables many clients to afford therapy.** With typical private-pay fees averaging $120 to $200 per session, your services may be out of the financial reach of much of the population. While they may love you and value therapy, it is a harsh reality that some potential clients would have to choose between much-needed therapy and paying the rent. For them, paying full fee – or even a sliding scale fee – cannot compare to paying a $15 copayment. Accepting insurance is one way to make therapy affordable and accessible, and see clients from diverse cultural and socioeconomic backgrounds.

► **Insurance may allow them to stay longer.** Even clients who can afford to pay privately for some therapy may be able to afford more treatment. I like to think of insurance as a type of subsidy or financial aid, which helps clients to partially finance ongoing treatment.

► **It's a way to attract the "therapy-avoidant."** Having insurance coverage brings in clients who might never have come to therapy. This is especially true of employee assistance programs (EAPs), since they are a free employee benefit, and advertised at the workplace. It may give clients a "taste of therapy," and they often choose to continue on their own after the EAP sessions have run out (for more about EAPs, see Chapter 3).

► **Holding on to clients, both old and new.** We've all had it happen – that great client who switches insurance plans, and tearfully informs you she has to leave since you don't take her new insurance, and she can't afford to pay your fee. Or the new client who calls after hearing great things about you, but requests a referral when he finds out you don't accept his insurance. Accepting a variety of insurance plans avoids this loss – of clients and income.

► **Free training/resources.** Some insurance companies offer free or low-cost webinars, workshops, or teleconferences for their participating providers on a wide variety of clinical issues. Some even offer free Continuing Education Units. Many health plans put out regular provider newsletters, and post helpful online articles and resources for clients and providers.

► **Private practice can be isolating.** Believe it or not, sometimes it is helpful to have a case manager to discuss your client with, who might be able to help with treatment adjuncts, resources you didn't know about, or benefits you didn't know the client had.

► **My personal reason?** Gratitude. When I first saw a therapist, I was a full-time graduate student living on ramen and generic mac and cheese. My husband's insurance helped me afford the therapy that changed my life. I am grateful every day for the opportunity insurance gave me. Accepting insurance is one way I can give this opportunity to others.

2
Understanding Insurance Plans
Decoding the Alphabet Soup

ೞ ೞ

There are few topics that stir such passionate feelings in the hearts of therapists as managed care and insurance. Much of this negative feeling is related to the frustration of trying to learn how to deal with a system which can be very confusing, especially to the newcomer. Also, the rules vary among insurance companies, and with each type of plan within a company, so it is nearly impossible to ever attain a feeling of competence.

To help you understand the types of insurance plans and the differences between them, it may help to use a case example.

Meet Jack

Jack comes to you at the urging of his wife, Jill. He reports he recently tripped over a pail of water and fell down a hill. Since the fall he has experienced recurring nightmares of the event, distressing recollections and flashbacks, hypervigilance, and has developed a phobic response when in the presence of a pail. Jack's anxiety has made it difficult to function in his job as a pail salesman at Pails "R" Us. Jack got your name from his insurance company, who we'll call CureQuick Insurance.

First, A Few Definitions

As Jack investigates his insurance coverage, he is faced with learning a new vocabulary. While I've included an extended glossary at the back of this book, let's start with some key concepts:

▶ **Deductible:** The dollar amount (usually yearly) that Jack has to pay before his insurance kicks in and begins to reimburse him for medical expenses. Not all plans have deductibles.

▶ **Copayment:** The <u>fixed, flat fee</u> that Jack's plan may require him to pay for each visit (after the deductible is exhausted, if any). The plan pays the rest of the allowed amount.

▶ **Co-insurance:** In some plans, instead of a copayment, Jack pays some <u>percentage</u> of the provider's fee (after the deductible is exhausted, if any). Insurance pays the rest of the allowed amount. In rare cases, a plan will have both a copayment and a coinsurance.

► **Provider network or panel:** These are the healthcare providers who have signed a contract with CureQuick to deliver services to Jack and other members of the CureQuick health plan. The providers usually agree to accept a fee discount and to file claims for the any CureQuick clients – this serves as an incentive for CureQuick clients to choose them.

Types of Mental Health Coverage

Jack is delighted to find out that Pails "R" Us has an employee assistance program. This program entitles all employees and dependents to three free sessions yearly with a counselor in CureQuick Insurance's Employee Assistance Program network.

Employee Assistance Program (EAP): This is an employee benefit provided by some employers who have agreed to cover all employees and dependents for a certain number of free counseling sessions per year (usually three to ten) with one of their EAP network providers. EAP therapists provide assessment, short-term counseling, and referral. An employee assistance program is typically offered by the employer <u>in addition to</u> the employee's other mental health benefits. That is, clients might be eligible to use their free EAP sessions before they begin using their other mental health benefits. The EAP may be offered by the same insurance company that manages their mental health benefits, or another entity altogether. Not all employers offer EAP programs for their employees, so your clients may not have this benefit (for more on EAPs, see Chapter 3, "Employee Assistance Programs").

Jack gets a lot out of his EAP sessions, so is happy to learn that after the EAP sessions he also has ongoing mental health coverage through CureQuick Insurance. However, he learns that CureQuick has many types of health insurance plans, and Pails "R" Us offers more than one type of plan to employees. He can't recall which type he signed up for at enrollment time.

After his EAP sessions, Jack may one of several kinds of managed mental health plans.

What's a managed care plan? Back in what some therapists recall as "the good old days," insurance plans were mostly "indemnity" plans, or fee-for-service. These plans would indemnify -- or reimburse -- Jack or his providers for health care expenses as they were incurred. Jack was free to choose any provider he wanted to see, as often as he liked, and after he satisfied his deductible and paid his copayment, eligible services would be covered by his insurance plan.

However, as health care costs rose each year, insurance companies responded by changing the structure of their health plans. These new "managed care" plans reduced costs in a variety of ways, including setting yearly session or spending limits, signing contracts with preferred providers willing to accept discounts, and requiring pre-authorization (pre-treatment approval from the insurance company) and treatment review.

What types of managed care plans are there? It would be impossible to list all managed care plan varieties and details, so the most common types are outlined on the next page.

1. **Health Maintenance Organization (HMO):** A HMO typically covers a higher degree of preventive care than other plans, in order to minimize later care costs. Jack chooses or is assigned a primary care physician (PCP) who coordinates his care and may make referrals to specialists (though typically Jack would not need a referral to see a therapist). A HMO may have central medical clinics such as those used by Kaiser Permanente, or it may

contract with a network of individual practitioners in the community. HMOs usually offer broader coverage and lower out-of-pocket expenses for the client than other plans. However, many clients don't realize that with a HMO the insurance company will only cover visits to network providers, and their care may undergo more scrutiny than with other plans. For the provider, HMOs typically represent the highest amount of oversight and paperwork. For the client, it is may represent lower copayment but be the least flexible health plan.

2. **Preferred Provider Organization (PPO):** PPOs are generally more flexible than HMOs. With a PPO, the insurance company will cover Jack's visits both to network and out-of-network providers, with higher benefits paid when he visits network providers. If he chooses a network provider, Jack will get the benefit of a participating provider fee discount, and typically would get a lower copayment and deductible, and the provider will file claims on his behalf. However, PPOs usually involve deductibles and larger copayments than HMOs. The provider's treatment is less frequently reviewed by the plan, authorizations aren't usually needed, and paperwork is usually limited to claims.

3. **Exclusive Provider Organization (EPO):** An EPO operates like a PPO, except that the insurance company will only cover Jack's visits to network providers. As with PPOs, he will get the benefit of a participating provider discount, and the provider will file claims. Jack typically won't need a physician referral or preauthorization but will usually be responsible for paying a copayment and deductible.

4. **Point-of-Service Plan (POS):** A sort of HMO/PPO hybrid, this plan offers a great deal of flexibility and choice. With a typical POS plan, Jack would have a two- or three-tiered plan, and could choose any of the benefit levels when seeking care. He could choose a therapist from Tier 1, which would allow him to choose any therapist on CureQuick's HMO panel, and then the plan would operate just like a normal HMO. He may instead obtain treatment from any participating provider in Tier 2, CureQuick's PPO network, and in this case the plan would then work like a normal PPO. Finally, he may have a third tier, permitting him to go outside of both networks, and be reimbursed when he sees an out-of-network provider. If he chooses Tiers 1 or 2, Jack will get the benefit of a participating provider discount, and the provider will file claims. Each tier typically represents higher out-of-pocket expenses for Jack than the one before it.

Confused? Let's put the different plans side by side and on the next page and compare them.

A Comparison of Typical Insurance Plans

	Are Out-of-Network Providers Covered?	Client's Usual Cost For Service	Who Files Claims?	Treatment Pre-Authorization Required?
EAP	No	Free, paid for by employer	Provider	Yes
HMO	No	Typically lowest copayments, usually no deductible	Provider	Sometimes, but depends on plan
PPO	Yes, but at a higher cost to the client	Usually deductible, lower costs for network providers, higher costs for out-of-network providers	Provider, if in-network; client generally does if visiting an out-of-network provider	Typically not
EPO	No	Typically have deductible and copayment	Provider	Typically not
POS	Yes, but at a higher cost to the client	Lowest costs for HMO providers, higher for PPO providers, highest for out-of-network providers	Provider, if in-network; client generally does if visiting an out-of-network provider	May be needed, especially if using HMO provider

Note: Plans vary greatly. Please consult the specific health care policy or contract for plan details.

Making Choices That Fit Your Practice

Hopefully you can see that as a therapist you have a lot of choice about how involved to get with insurance.

Your first decision will be whether to become a network provider, or to accept insurance as an out-of-network therapist, or some combination of these two options (though remember, not all plans cover out-of-network providers). Let's review.

If You are a Network (Panel) Provider:

▶ **Pros:** You should get new client referrals from the insurance company and their website which may reduce your need for marketing. You'll be able to retain clients who have insurance and can't afford to pay privately.

▶ **Cons:** You must sign a contract with the plan. You typically accept a discounted rate for services, and must bill the insurance plan yourself. You may not "balance-bill" the client -- that is, you cannot bill your client for the portion of your full fee that insurance doesn't pay, since you agreed to accept the discounted fee when you signed the contract. Treatment may need to be pre-authorized and reviewed.

If You are an Out-of-Network Provider:

All providers who have not signed a contract with the insurance plan are considered out-of-network providers.

▶ **Pros:** You don't have to sign any contract with the insurance plan. You do not have to discount your fee. Clients can pay you in full and you give them an invoice -- also known as a "Superbill"-- to submit themselves (see sample invoice on 145). Your treatment usually will not need to be pre-authorized.

▶ **Cons:** You won't get new client referrals from the insurance company – you'll need to market your practice. Clients may leave you (or not come to you) and instead find a network provider on their plan, since this may be substantially less expensive for them.

It's important to keep in mind that <u>whenever you or your client submits a bill to an insurance plan, your treatment is subject to review, whether or not you are a network provider</u>.

The chart on the following page is another way of looking at your choices. It outlines the choices of two therapists who have selected different involvement levels with managed care, and how those decisions work for them.

Nina has decided she wants to take insurance but doesn't want to join any provider networks. She wants to avoid the paperwork and discounts she knows are part of the managed care world, so she chooses to be an out-of-network provider only.

Mark has gone for insurance "whole hog." He joins every network that will take him, hoping to fill those empty slots in his practice. He is willing to do the paperwork, and take some discounts in exchange for the referrals.

A Tale of Two Therapists: Two Extremes of Provider Participation

	Nina (No Managed Care): Out-of-Network Provider only	Mark (Mr. Managed Care): Network Provider for Many Plans
Can Accept What Insurance Plans?	▶ PPO out-of-network (if license is covered by plan) ▶ POS out-of-network (if license is covered by plan)	▶ EAP ▶ HMO ▶ PPO ▶ POS ▶ EPO
How Much Can Therapist Charge?	Therapist's full fee	Agrees to accept discounted fee. <u>Cannot</u> bill clients to make up for any fee discount
Amount of Paperwork	Typically minimal, may only involve claim form or invoice/superbill (see invoice sample on Page 145)	Depends on company. Once accepted on panel, paperwork may include surveys for client to complete, claims, and written requests for more sessions
Must Therapist Submit Claims?	No. Client pays full fee and therapists give client an invoice or superbill to submit to the plan (see sample invoice Page 145)	Yes
Will Insurance Refer Clients?	No	Yes, directly (phone) and indirectly (via printed or online provider directories)

Tax-Advantaged Savings Accounts; HSAs, MSAs, HRAs, and FSAs

As employers look for new ways to share the burden of rising health costs with their employees, new types of plans have emerged. Some employers offer these instead of more traditional health plans.

1. <u>**Health Savings Accounts (HSA) or Medical Savings Accounts (MSA)**</u>: Many employers offer employees a health savings account, which allows the employee to set aside pre-tax dollars from their income for future medical expenses. Contributions to the account can be made by your client, his employer, or both. If Jack had an HSA, he would be given choices on how to invest these funds, and then can use the funds to reimburse his qualified health expenses during the year. It's as if Jack put aside money in a piggy bank throughout the year and then when it came time to pay a healthcare provider, he could pay himself back out of this piggy bank. Except in this case, if he chose to save the money for future health expenses, the account would grow through investment earnings.

Jack would need to be enrolled in a high-deductible health plan and he could have no other major insurance coverage. The funds can roll over from year to year and are portable. He could take them with him if he changed jobs, changed medical coverage, became unemployed, or moved.

HSAs and MSAs allow a lot of choice, including how much to put in the account, what expenses to pay out of it, and what investments to make. Jack could even use the funds to pay for approved health expenses his insurance doesn't cover (such as for over-the-counter medications or bandages), or save the money for future health needs. And because of the high deductible, Jack may have a very low premium.

Perhaps the most attractive benefit of all? The account provides Jack with triple tax savings: deductions when he contributes to the account, tax-free earnings through investment, and tax-free withdrawals for qualified medical expenses.

Some clients will ask their therapist for an invoice for any paid amounts so they can submit it to their HSA or MSA for reimbursement. Other plans allow clients to use the money in their accounts to reimburse providers directly for their portion of the costs -- clients may have access to these accounts via checks or debit cards, so you could be reimbursed in this way. With some plans you bill the health plan as if it was a regular insurance plan, and the provider is simply paid directly out of the member's account. Check with the health plan in advance for instructions.

2. <u>**Health Reimbursement Arrangements (HRA)**</u>: Very similar to a HSA account -- the main difference between a HRA and a HSA is that HRA funds are provided only by an employer for an employee.

3. **Flexible Spending Accounts (FSA):** This account allows for reimbursement of childcare, dependent care, and/or health care expenses, and enables employees to pay for these expenses with a non-taxed portion of their salary. The main difference between a FSA and a HSA is that FSA funds typically must be used within the calendar year or they are forfeited. Therefore, if Jack guesses he will be paying about $2000 in the coming year for childcare and medical expenses, he will have his employer deduct this amount from his salary over the course of that year. His employer would deposit these pre-tax payroll deductions into his (non-interest-bearing) FSA. Anytime Jack submits an invoice from a medical or child-care provider, he would be reimbursed with funds from his account.

A client with a FSA does not need a high-deductible insurance plan. As with MSAs, some clients will ask for an invoice for any paid amounts so they can submit it to their FSA for reimbursement. Other plans allow clients to use the money in their accounts to reimburse providers directly, via checks or debit cards.

3

Employee Assistance Programs
ಹ ಛ

As mentioned in the previous chapter, an employee assistance program (EAP) is a benefit provided by many employers who cover their employees and dependents for a certain number of free counseling sessions per year (usually three to ten) with one of their EAP network providers. EAP therapists provide assessment, short-term counseling, and referral. Studies have shown that by offering this program to workers, employers can minimize absences, improve productivity, and in other ways contain the employer's cost of illness.

An employee assistance program is in addition to (and usually separate from) other mental health coverage the client might have through their medical insurance. Clients usually use their free EAP sessions before they access their other mental health benefits.

Jack's employer may have an internal EAP, in which the EAP counseling office is located at the workplace, and the EAP therapists are on the company payroll. Or the EAP may be external, made up of a network of community providers. In Jack's case, Pails "R" Us has hired the CureQuick network of providers to provide both the EAP and ongoing mental health insurance for its employees. Sometimes the same insurance plan will provide both EAP and mental health sessions; in other cases, a separate EAP firm may provide EAP services.

It is unfortunate that not everyone has an employee assistance program. It is also unfortunate that clients who <u>do</u> have this benefit often aren't aware of it. You could try to ask the health insurance plan when you call, but if the EAP plan is handled by a separate firm, the client's health plan may not be aware of the EAP coverage. Particularly for clients concerned about therapy cost, you might suggest that the client talk to his employer's human resources department or check his benefits manual.

Clients are often pleasantly surprised to find that their EAP plan may offer other types of assistance, such as a few free sessions of legal consultation, financial advice or credit counseling, tax assistance, eldercare or childcare referral assistance, educational and career support and referrals, mediation services, and retirement planning. However, these visits may count against the client's total number of allotted EAP sessions.

When a client uses an EAP, it is important to keep in mind:

- ▶ **Pre-authorization is always needed.**

- ▶ **There is no "out-of-network" EAP option.** Clients must see a participating EAP provider.

- ▶ **EAP sessions are free for the client.**

- ▶ **Sessions are typically very limited in number (3-6).** You don't usually have the option of getting more until the following year. Sometimes if there is a new presenting issue they will allow you to count this as a separate event, and grant additional sessions. However, some occupations offer unlimited EAP sessions (such as some fire and police departments).

- ▶ **Sessions are confidential.** EAP clients often worry that what they share will be shared with their employers. This is not the case, though some information may be shared if counseling is mandated by the workplace or court (for more on confidentiality, see Chapter 15).

- ▶ **No diagnosis of mental illness is necessary.** Clients may see an EAP therapist to discuss any issue, and do not need to have a diagnosis. This is not typically the case with other types of mental health coverage. In addition, the sessions don't need to be "medically necessary" (more on this in Chapter 9).

- ▶ **Your role as an EAP provider is to provide assessment, referral, and brief problem resolution.** One insurance plan puts it this way: "EAP providers are most effective when they think of themselves as the early architects of a member's recovery rather than the means to that recovery."[5] Another says "EAP counseling is typically present-centered and does not seek extensive exploration or attempted resolution of long-term family of origin issues."[6] So be sure to set realistic goals and treatment plans within the given time frame. If the client continues in therapy past the EAP sessions, goals can be modified at that time.

- ▶ **Follow-up may be expected.** As an EAP provider you may be expected to follow-up with clients after the EAP sessions are over if a referral was made (and sometimes even if no referral was made). Document any follow-up (or attempts) in the client's record. You may also be expected to call the health plan and close the EAP case when you are done. Some even expect a brief summary of treatment.

Questions and Answers

I'm confused. Sometimes the letters "EAP" seems to be used to refer to the program. At other times it seems to refer to the counselor working in the program.

You're right – and it can be confusing. The initials EAP may stand for "Employee Assistance Program" or it may refer to "Employee Assistance Professional," the title of the clinician providing the services for the employee assistance program.

Can anyone apply to become an EAP provider?

It depends on the network. Some plans are simply looking for providers who can demonstrate experience and/or education in assessment, short-term problem resolution, and referral. They typically want to see good brief therapy and crisis intervention skills and chemical dependency assessment experience. However, most seem to require EAP experience or special certification before they will put you on their "sub-network" of EAP providers. This makes getting your foot in the door more of a problem. Value Options health plan, for example, requires either 1) active status as a Certified Employee Assistance Professional (CEAP), or 2) two years of verifiable experience as an internal EAP counselor, and/or as an external EAP consultant to other organizations.[7] Managed Health Network requires CEAP status or "1,500 hours of combined training and experience that resulted in expertise in the following areas: addiction counseling, job-related issues/performance improvement, short–term counseling, family and relationship counseling, assessment and referral."[8] United Behavioral Health asks some applicants to fill out a questionnaire about their EAP or related experience, including a multiple-choice quiz on their understanding of EAPs and the handling of hypothetical cases.[9]

Can Jack get more EAP sessions after he has used his maximum, if he needs them?

Clients are usually limited to one batch of free sessions per year. However, some EAP benefits are not "per benefit year," they are "per incident," or "per problem type." Under these plans, Jack could use his EAP benefits more than once a year if he had different presenting issues on intake. Even with these types of plans, many EAP programs have a maximum number of allowable sessions per "contract year" (contracts are not always based on a calendar year). Some clients -- especially those in high-stress or high-risk jobs, such as police, firefighters, and paramedics -- may have EAP plans that allow them to access the EAP anytime.

Why was my client referred directly to her ongoing mental health coverage for treatment, rather than to her EAP benefits?

At intake, your client's EAP counselor may have felt that she needed longer-term treatment than could be provided in the EAP sessions, so referred the client directly to use her managed care plan's covered mental health sessions. This may include clients with suicidal or homicidal ideation, severe or chronic mental illness, active substance abuse, or the need for immediate or more long-term treatment.

Can I just bill the EAP as I would for any other insurance session?

This depends on the plan. Many EAPs have their own claim forms, which they'll often send with the authorization. You will sometimes be asked to wait to bill for sessions until all EAP sessions are completed. You may need to attach a closed case form or case information form which summarizes treatment. Many companies will not pay without these forms. If the client has both EAP and ongoing mental health benefits with the same health plan, and both allow you to use a universal CMS-1500 claim form (more about this in Chapter 11), it is wise to bill the EAP sessions on a separate page to avoid confusion. Also, some plans may require you to use a different CPT code for EAP sessions (more on CPT codes in Chapter 11). Ask the plan.

What other roles do EAP providers play?

EAP therapists also assist employers by providing Critical Incident Stress Debriefings (CISD), consultations to employers, mandated employer and employee trainings (e.g. sexual harassment or chemical dependency), employee wellness/mental health seminars, and by representing the EAP at employee health fairs.

Will Employee Assistance Programs pay for missed appointments or late-cancelled sessions?

Usually not, but check your contract. One plan I work for pays $25 for the first missed session. Some will allow you to deduct a session from the client's total EAP benefit for each missed session. Some will not allow you even to bill the client for the missed session. Others allow you to bill the client if the client has previously agreed (in writing) to pay for missed sessions.

What are Jack's options if he needs further treatment when his EAP sessions end?

One of the following scenarios is possible for Jack:

1. **Jack's CureQuick EAP sessions may be all the mental health coverage he has.** This is rare. However, in this case, you will have to refer him to appropriate and affordable community resources, or, if allowed, it may be possible to continue to see him in your private-pay practice (see next question below).
2. **Jack may have further mental health benefits, also handled by CureQuick.** You might then refer him to a CureQuick network therapist, possibly even yourself.
3. **Jack may have further mental health benefits, handled by another insurance company.** You might then refer him to a therapist within the other company's network, possibly even yourself.

So, Jack can continue working privately with me after the EAP sessions are over?

Well, that depends. Some companies have no problem with "self-referral". Treatment must, of course, be within the scope of your competence and practice, and it is wise to give (and document that you gave) alternate referrals. However, many companies do not allow self-referral: They do not want referral decisions to appear clouded by a therapist's desire to fill an empty therapy slot in his or her practice. The professional guidelines of the Employee Assistance Professionals Association state that "any actual or perceived conflict of interest among EAP professionals and service providers shall be avoided."[10] Contact the insurance company to ask their policy.

Even companies that do not allow self-referral may make exceptions in certain situations. These situations may include when:
1. Continuity of treatment would enable successful and most rapid closure of clinical issues.
2. Disruption of service with you might place the client at risk.
3. You are working on an issue in which you possess an unusual expertise.
4. There are no available participating network providers in the same geographic area.

The private-pay agreement: If Jack has no further coverage, but wants to continue to see you (and your EAP contract allows self-referral), it is a good idea to have him sign a private-pay agreement (a sample agreement can be found on Page 143). This agreement states that he understands his therapy is no longer covered by insurance, and he is now responsible for paying your full fee (or one that you have negotiated with him). Signing this type of agreement protects you from having Jack come back later, saying he didn't understand that his sessions would no longer be covered by the plan.

If I see Jack as a private-pay client after the EAP, can I charge my usual fee?

Usually, yes. However, I know of at least one EAP firm whose contract states that if you continue privately with Jack after his EAP sessions, you must stick to the EAP discounted rate for these private sessions. For this type of contract, if you have discounted your rate to $60 for CureQuick's EAP clients, you may only charge Jack $60 if you continue to see him in your private practice when his EAP benefits have ended. Read your contract. It may be a point worth trying to negotiate.

What about management referrals, also known as mandatory or supervisor referrals?

Managers, supervisors, and human resources personnel can formally refer employees whose personal problems are affecting the workplace or work performance. These management referrals require special handling. Even if they involve voluntary attendance by the employee, but an employee may not be able to return to work and may be on unpaid leave until he reports to an EAP counselor or completes treatment.

Contrary to popular belief, in most cases the EAP counselor is <u>not</u> expected to contact the supervisor or employer directly. In my experience, attendance and/or progress information is given only to the case manager at the EAP plan. What will the case manager tell the supervisor or manager? A typical policy is articulated by Value Options EAP in their client treatment agreement: "If you were formally referred to EAP by your supervisor, he or she will be provided the following non-clinical information: a) whether or not you have followed through in contacting the EAP; b) whether or not a problem has been identified and if a program treatment has been recommended; c) whether or not you are participating and complying with your treatment plan. Note: your supervisor will <u>not</u> be given clinical information about the specifics of your problems."[11]

In our example, Jack would sign a release of information to allow his employee assistance program administrators (not you) to speak with his supervisor or manager. The release is limited to the information outlined above. Even though the client may understand that in these cases the sharing of information is a condition of treatment, it is a good idea to discuss the types of information you are being asked to release, and to whom you will be releasing it, and have the client complete your own release of information before making any disclosures.

If a client discusses harassment issues, worker's compensation, company wrongdoing, or legal action, this may limit their confidentiality. It is advised that you get legal consultation and talk to the client about these confidentiality issues, and talk to the case manager at the EAP program before making recommendations to the client that would support pursuing litigation or filing complaints against the employer or insurance company.

What if Jack asks me to write a letter excusing him from work? What if I am asked to fill out disability paperwork or fitness-for-duty determinations?

The EAP is not a medical service, so providers can't fill out disability paperwork or determine if an employee is fit for duty. In general, you should avoid any verbal or written correspondence with the client's employer regarding the client's ability to work or any other aspect of treatment. This is usually outside the scope of our practice and training as psychotherapists, and is better left for the client's doctor or psychiatrist. You may be asked to answer questions for a state or private disability firm about the client's symptoms if the disability is related to mental health, but avoid subjective comments or making evaluations of fitness for duty.

4

Horror Stories: Myth or Reality?

ಹ ಛ

When therapists explain why they have chosen not to accept insurance, it often becomes clear that their decision was based (at least in part) on misinformation or myths. Let's explore some myths about getting involved with insurance:

Myth? "If I take insurance, I'll have to do billing, and lots of paperwork.

The facts: There's no denying that insurance involves paperwork. How much depends on your choices. If you loathe the idea of billing, you can choose to take insurance as an out-of-network provider, collect your full fee, and provide an invoice or superbill the client can submit to the insurance plan (see sample invoice Page 145). Or, if you want referrals but not a lot of paperwork, you might join just a few plans, and accept mostly PPO clients. Or you can simply limit the number of insurance clients you take, so that the paperwork is also limited. A final option would be to only join plans that require minimal provider paperwork.

Myth? "If I take insurance, I'll have to discount my fee."

The facts: As was discussed in Chapter 2, you only need to take fee discounts when you become a participating provider. Let's say Jack has a PPO that covers 80 percent for network providers but only 50 percent for out-of-network providers. As an out-of-network provider, you could simply collect your full fee (e.g. $100) from Jack and provide him with a statement he can submit to CureQuick.

Should you choose to become a participating provider, there is no getting around it — the reduced fee is by far the biggest complaint of most panel therapists. But some therapists feel it may be worth taking the discount for the referrals -- a discounted fee may be better than an empty slot -- and for the other reasons outlined in Chapter 1.

Myth? "If I take insurance, I'll have to do brief therapy, and sessions will be limited."

The facts: Yes, it's true that in the past, most plans had yearly session limitations. And plans are looking for therapists who are skilled in brief therapy. However, this doesn't mean they won't cover long-term treatment. <u>And due to the Affordable Care Act and federal parity laws, most plans now must allow unlimited sessions for mental health</u> if the sessions are deemed to be medically necessary by the plan (for more on parity laws, see Page 31; the Affordable Care Act, see Page 36; and medical necessity, see Page 48).

Myth? "If I take insurance, my therapy will be micro-managed by idiots at the insurance companies."

The facts: While in the past case managers were often unlicensed clerks, these days they are usually licensed Master's-level clinicians. In my experience, while plans will occasionally call to discuss cases, these are typically not routine cases – they are the more complex, lengthy, or chronic cases. And such treatment reviews are probably rarer than most therapists imagine. In over 20 years I have only been reviewed a handful of times, and I have never felt micro-managed. In my experience most plans do not make routine requests for treatment plans, and those that do are typically approved. However, since federal parity laws took effect in 2010, most plans must offer unlimited sessions if the sessions are medically necessary, so it is possible that plans may begin doing more medical necessity reviews (see Page 48 for more on this).

Myth? "All the networks are full."

The facts: While it is true that many insurance panels say they are full, they make exceptions every day, accepting new applicants if they need someone with their skills, experience, language abilities, location, or because they need to diversify their panel in some way. It is unpredictable, so you should always apply, and keep applying (for more about joining plans, see Chapter 5). Even those plans that are full today have changing needs. The plan may land a new employer account in your area tomorrow, and be scrambling to dig through their files for resumes from providers in your area who have previously expressed interest.

Myth? "If I take insurance, my clients will have to get a doctor referral to see me."

The facts: Long ago, a pre-treatment doctor referral was required by many insurance plans, so this impression persists. However, times have changed, and almost all plans now allow client self-referral -- no doctor referral required. Even if they require pre-authorization, this is usually something the client or provider can get over the phone from the health plan, without a doctor referral.

Myth? "If I take insurance, I'll have to give diagnoses to clients who aren't mentally ill."

The facts: While it is true that health plans only cover mental illness, this includes adjustment disorders and other non-severe mental illnesses. Also, employee assistance programs don't require diagnoses. Remember, it is insurance fraud to give a diagnosis where none exists. If you cannot justify a diagnosis, the client should be told that you cannot in good faith bill the medical insurance plan, and the client can always choose to pay out of pocket. Do not fall into the trap of giving all your clients the same diagnosis, one you feel can't hurt them. This is fraud (more on diagnosis and fraud, Page 100).

Myth? "If I take insurance, I'll have to deal with HIPAA."

The facts: Accepting insurance does *not* automatically mean you become a "covered entity" under the Health Insurance Portability and Accountability Act (HIPAA), or that you have to comply with the requirements of HIPAA. Most lawyers interpret HIPAA to only apply to you if you will be communicating any confidential client private health information electronically (usually via the Internet) or if you have someone else conducting these transactions electronically on your behalf. However, there are good reasons why all therapists should become knowledgeable about and compliant with HIPAA regulations. For more information about HIPAA, see Chapter 7.

5

Becoming a Network Provider
Selling Yourself to Insurance Companies

⊗ ⊗

I like to say that in the "good old days," all you needed to have to join a provider network was a pulse. While that may be an exaggeration, many panels required little more than an application and resume. Those days are gone. In most areas of the country, if the network isn't already full, insurance companies can afford to be choosy, in part because there are more therapists applying.

Since it is expensive to develop and maintain a provider network and database, it is in a plan's best interest to maintain the fewest possible providers on their network. However, many plans are required to maintain minimum "density standards" (the required number of providers in any given region). They also must meet the varied clinical needs of their members in your area.

So, let's say you have decided to join a provider panel. Where do you start?

> ▶ **Get a list of insurance companies** that may cover your services. Your professional organization or state Department of Insurance (DOI) may have a list of insurance companies that operate in your area, with contact numbers and addresses.

> ▶ **Ask colleagues what provider panels they belong to**, and about their experiences with the plan, and for contact information.

> ▶ **Call each insurance plan, or go to the plan's website to apply.** On the phone, ask for Provider Contracting or Network Development. If the network is "closed," this means the plan is (allegedly) not accepting new providers in your area. But don't take no for an answer – plans will always make exceptions. Ask about plan needs, and sell yourself. If you have a needed specialty, have an office in a less populated area, see children and adolescents, treat veterans, specialize in substance abuse, treat ADD/autism, can see clients on weekends, or can conduct sessions in another language, let them know — they might make an exception for you (see page 23 for a list of what they are looking for).

▶ **If closed, don't be deterred.** I suggest you send a letter of interest and targeted "managed care resume" to sell yourself to the plan, asking for an application (for more on what to include in this letter and resume, see the following sections).

> _**Tip:**_ _Eventually, perhaps through attrition, there will be openings on the panel. Every three to six months, resubmit a letter of interest with your managed care resume. Try to target your letter to a specific person, or, failing that, to "Manager, Network Development" or "Manager, Provider Relations." Try to follow-up by phone or e-mail, and if possible speak to your target person._

▶ **Keep a communication log** with dates of your calls, names of the people you spoke with, their responses, and action taken.

▶ **While most insurance companies will NOT accept interns or social work associates** as network providers (in fact, most require that you have been licensed two to three years), some interns have found plans that will reimburse them and even accept them on the plan if they have very unique skills or languages or are in an underserved location. So ask around. Also try smaller and regional plans.

▶ **Consider forming a group.** Panels like the idea of contracting with provider groups, when possible. A provider group is usually defined as a group of providers who share the same billing tax ID, and a unified billing process.

Why You Should Have a "Managed Care Resume"

Because plans can afford to be picky when accepting new providers, your resume is very important. But chances are your current resume may not be the best, and may even contain things that could jeopardize your acceptance. I strongly urge you to prepare a "managed care resume," designed to give you an edge when applying, and to highlight the experience and training you have that plans are looking for. I recommend a resume that:

▶ **Begins with a summary (in bullet form) of your specialties and qualifications** (see the lists on previous pages for the type of items to emphasize)
▶ **Includes a list of places of employment,** job titles, job descriptions, degrees, licenses, professional affiliations, and relevant lectures given or groups facilitated
▶ **Is brief** -- page, if possible, two maximum. Since insurers are flooded with resumes, they are unlikely to read a three page resume.
▶ **Helps you stand out.** You need to think hard about how you are different from the therapist in the next office, and make that clear.
▶ **Contains those all-important managed care buzzwords,** such as "symptom-reduction focus," "problem-solving therapy" and "cognitive-behavioral treatment."

The problem is most therapists are not great at selling themselves. So get help with writing this (if you need help writing your managed care resume, see insurance consultants listed in Resources, Page 133).

Your Letter of Interest

When applying to a managed care plan, write a letter of interest to include with your resume. Keep it to one page. It should start with a request to become a provider on their behavioral health network panel. Think about the following topics you might highlight before writing your letter, and pick information that shows you in the best light.

► **Specialties/training:** What skills set you apart from colleagues? These may include working with eating disorders, children, ADD/autism, veterans and military families, PTSD/trauma, or gay and lesbian issues.
► **Brief therapy/crisis intervention** training and treatment experience
► **Substance abuse** training, assessment, and treatment experience
► **Managed care/EAP experience:** Mention the number of years of experience as a managed care or EAP provider, or your familiarity with managed care expectations.
► **Location:** Highlight your location's strengths, especially if in an underserved area
► **Availability:** e.g. large number of open hours available for members, or at times when other therapists traditionally are not, such as weekends
► **Current members:** Mention if you are seeing a large number of the plan's members
► **Language:** Can you conduct therapy in another language? Sign-language?
► **Ethnic/cultural diversity:** Insurance plans seek therapists of diverse gender, race, ethnicity, and cultures. Cross-cultural competency is also valued.
► **Coordination of care:** Tell them about hospital privileges or willingness to treat clients in the hospital or after discharge, and if you work closely with physicians and other treating providers
► **Groups/Classes:** Let them know if you offer therapy/support groups, or psycho-educational classes. You could include a flier from a group you are leading, a brochure from a workshop you are teaching, if it markets your uniqueness
► **Electronic billing** (may even be required by some plans, such as TriCare, and UBH.

Panel Applications

So you are finally sent an application, or fill one out online. Yippee! Now what will you be asked? It varies with the plan, but it may include:

► **Theoretical orientation:** Insurers may ask you to describe your theoretical orientation, and often provide a checklist. Most insurance companies are looking for therapists competent in short-term therapy, cognitive-behavioral treatment, and crisis intervention. If you check off only "psychodynamic" or "psychoanalytic," this could put your application in the recycle bin.

► **Percentage of cases ended in 5, 10, 15, 20+ sessions:** Again, while they understand you'll have longer term cases, they are looking for therapists who are able to provide short-term, problem-focused treatment. They'll typically want to see most treatment ending in less than 20 sessions.

► **Your availability.** Plans are looking for providers who will have enough openings for their members, so may not accept you if only work park time – if you do, sell them on your availability to see their members. EAPs especially like to see evening

23

or weekend availability. In addition, many plans use the National Committee for Quality Assurance (NCQA)'s availability standards, looking for therapists who can schedule routine appointments for new clients within ten business days, routine appointments for current clients within 14 days, urgent cases within 48 hours, and non-life-threatening emergency cases within six hours. In life-threatening emergencies, some type of help should be available immediately by phone.[12] They may check up on this by contacting you to check availability, or by asking clients how long they waited for a session.

▶ **After-hours/vacation coverage:** Many companies require some form of 24-hour coverage for your clients. They also may want your outgoing answering machine message to instruct clients on how to reach you (or a covering therapist) in an emergency or to direct them to go to a nearby emergency room or dial 911.

▶ **License, malpractice, and CEUs:** Applications typically will ask you to attach a copy of your license, malpractice insurance (they may have certain coverage minimums), and to list your Continuing Education Units from the past few years.

▶ **Your friends.** They may ask for professional organizations you belong to, and the names of psychiatrists you refer to, and colleagues who can vouch for you.

▶ **Any history of trouble.** They may ask about past malpractice claims, or if you've ever had your license, privileges, or professional membership revoked. If you have, you may need to submit legal documents to show settlements and dispositions.

▶ **They may ask you to sign a release** to allow them to check out the information you've given them, from schools, malpractice, references, licensing boards, etc.

▶ **They may ask you to visit CAQH.** The Council for Affordable Quality Healthcare's Universal Provider Datasource is a free, centralized, standard online application form, where providers are able to enter their information, and plans nationwide can view it, with your permission. But it is a club you can't join without an invitation – the interested plan needs to assign you a CAQH Provider ID from before you can visit the CAQH website and fill out the application. CAQH is not an insurance plan -- think of it as a secure bulletin board where you post your application information and plans can visit if they want to learn more about you.

▶ **If the application you receive includes a provider contract**, this doesn't mean you have been accepted yet. *Read it carefully.* Legal jargon isn't always easy to understand, so call the plan with questions. It is sometimes possible to negotiate a contract provision or even fees before joining. Watch out for special provisions. One EAP program may allow you to continue privately with a client after sessions are exhausted, but only at the discounted fee. Another may state that you cannot continue to see a client after EAP sessions end. Make notes about different policies so you don't accidently breach the contract, which can put you in hot water.

▶ **Go over the application thoroughly before submitting.** Even a complete application can take three to nine months to be processed -- you don't want to leave out any information that could delay the process. Don't leave blanks -- Write "none" or "N/A" to show you didn't overlook the question. Keep copies of everything in case your application is lost.

Single Case Agreements and Transition of Care Agreements

A Single Case Agreement means that for one client only, an out-of-network therapist is treated as a network therapist. This is typically done only in special situations, such as when there is a change of insurance plans during the client's treatment, when there is no network therapist with appropriate qualifications who is available (or within reasonable driving distance of the client), or all available professionals have some type of dual role. It may also be used when the provider is going through the credentialing process. Sometimes you may be able to receive a reimbursement rate that is higher than the network rate, or even your full fee.

If Jack's insurance changes, and you are not a network provider for his new plan, you may be able to receive a certain number of "Transition of Care" (TOC) sessions from the new plan. The idea is that the new plan agrees to cover a certain number of sessions while Jack is transitioned to a network provider at the new plan, if ongoing treatment is needed. However, Jack may choose to just use these TOC sessions and then pay you out of pocket if he chooses to continue with you.

It is better to have Jack make a TOC request to the plan, but the therapist can also initiate this request. Usually, a case manager from the plan will need to approve the request, and you'll need to fill out some paperwork to agree to a negotiated fee and to abide by plan policies. You will need to collect the client's copayment and submit claims for this client.

Unfortunately, such temporary network status rarely becomes permanent, except in cases where you fill a deficit in the network.

Before you pursue this option, you may want to find out if he has out-of-network benefits, and explore the pros and cons of going this route instead

Questions and Answers

What kind of reimbursement can I expect?

Fees vary depending on a variety of factors, including the insurance company, the type of plan, your educational level, your location, your license, and whether you've ever negotiated a rate increase. The table below reports national averages from a 2005 *Psychotherapy Finances* subscriber survey.[13] While this information is quite dated, and some plans pay more, providers from all over the country complain to me daily that rates have increased little or not at all since then.

Most Frequent Fees Paid for Individual Therapy
Psychotherapy Finances, Fee and Practice Survey, 2005

	Managed Care
MFTs	$60
Professional Counselors	$63
Psychologists	$75
Social Workers	$60

Can I negotiate my fee or anything in the contract before joining?

Good luck. Provider contracts and fee structures are fairly standard, and most plans won't negotiate them up front. Unless you have something insurers might be willing to pay extra for (e.g., some valuable specialty, skill, language fluency, weekend hours, or if they are in need of providers in your area), it is unlikely they will raise your rates before they have had a chance to evaluate your performance, or get client feedback. However, other than potentially delaying your application, it can't hurt to try! (For more on raises, see Page 122).

How long does it usually take for them to process my application?

It varies greatly between companies, but the wait can sometimes be three to nine months.

Once I am accepted, am I in for good?

Insurance companies will require that you go through a less-extensive recredentialing process every two or three years, to be sure that they still want you in the network. They want to update your practice information, but they will also review information in your provider file, including any member complaints, and statistics on client satisfaction and length of average client stay.

While filling out recredentialing paperwork is a hassle, it's important – if you don't do it in a timely manner, you may be dropped from the network. Health plans are trying to streamline this time-consuming and costly process. Many plans have now contracted with third-party Credentialing Verification Organizations (CVOs), such as CAQH Universal Credentialing DataSource (UCD) or Aperture (see Resources, Page 133). As was described earlier, CAQH allows you to complete a single application online to meet the credentialing needs of multiple insurance plans. Once you submit your practice data, participating plans no longer need to contact you directly with recredentialing forms to seek the necessary information. You will then simply need to update your information regularly with CAQH.

Should I pay a fee to join?

Application fees are rare, and should be cause for caution. Many therapists I know paid fees to join a plan and never received any referrals. If you are considering a network that charges a fee, ask about other providers' experience with that company. *Psychotherapy Finances* also suggests you investigate the company: "Is the company actually providing mental health care coverage to clients, or just printing and distributing a list of providers?"[14]

I have a home office. Is this okay?

Some insurance companies accept home offices, but others won't. If they do, they may have certain requirements. The office, client entrance, waiting area, and client restroom may need to be separate from the living area, used only for business, and you may need a dedicated office phone line. A site visit may be required to certify the space is suitable. United Behavioral Health tells clinicians they must notify clients in advance that the office is in the home, warn of pets, and offer off-street parking. UBH will not allow high-risk or potentially violent clients to be seen in the home, so telephone screening must be done prior to the first appointment.[15]

6

Talking to the Insurance Plan
Who to Talk To, How to Get Through

ಬ ಐ

How do you know who to call for what? The hierarchy and titles vary with the company, but let's take a minute to review the relevant "cast list" at an average insurance company.

Administrative Staff

► **Provider Relations Representative:** Deals with all provider-related questions. May handle applications, recredentialing, provider information changes, reimbursement rate increase requests, and other administrative duties.

► **Customer Service Representative:** Don't be fooled by the title — these folks can be very helpful to providers. While not clinicians, these unsung heroes of the insurance company can handle most non-clinical issues, including answering your basic questions about a client's benefits, coverage, and claims handling.

► **Claims Representative:** Handles all claims-related issues, such as unpaid claims, adjustments, overpayments, underpayments, and claims denials.

Clinical Staff

► **Intake Worker:** This might be your client's first contact, if your client called the plan, or needed pre-authorization for treatment. The intake worker takes basic clinical information about the presenting problem, assesses for risk factors, makes referrals to appropriate network providers, and gives initial authorizations for treatment.

▶ **Case Manager/Care Manager:** Clients may be assigned a case manager who handles the therapist's requests for additional sessions and handles any clinical issues that arise during treatment. Or there may be a case management team that handles all calls relating to members from a specific employer.

▶ **Clinical Director/Medical Director:** Advises the case management team on high-risk or difficult cases and proposed denials. Develops treatment policies and guidelines for the company. It is rare that you'd interact with them, except in extreme clinical crises or possibly to request an exception to plan policies.

▶ **Appeals Department:** If your request for additional treatment or your claim is denied, and you appeal, these are the folks who will review your appeal.

Navigating the Automated Phone System

It isn't always easy to get through to the right person at an insurance company. In fact, it isn't easy to get through to a person at all. But here are some tips to keep in mind:

▶ **What time is it there?** Make sure you call during normal business hours in the time zone of the insurance company's headquarters. If you are located on the West Coast, this may mean calling before 1:00 or 2:00 pm. After normal business hours you may reach a recorded message. Even if you do reach a live person, the after-hours staff may have limited ability to help you. They may only be available to assist with clinical emergencies, and sometimes can help with referrals.

▶ **Allow yourself enough time to make the call.** Five or ten minutes between clients is typically not enough to unsnarl a claim or authorization problem. Running out of time and having to call back will only add to your frustration.

▶ **Before you dial, take a deep breath.** Get all your paperwork together. Be ready to give the client's name, date of birth, insurance identification number, social security number, and group number, as well as your name, phone number, and tax ID number (your Social Security Number or Employer ID Number) and National Provider ID number (NPI), if you have one. If you are calling about a claim, know the claim ID, the date(s) of service, and full amount you charged.

▶ **Formulate your question or problem and desired outcome concisely,** so you can be routed to the correct person. Be patient and friendly.

▶ **Leaving a message?** Leave as much identifying information as possible. This may include your name, phone number with area code (repeated), the client's name (spelled out), the insured's name, plan ID number, client's date of birth, the date(s) of service in question, the charged amount (if it is a claims issue), and details about your problem. If leaving clinical details, be specific. A sample message follows:

"Hi, this is Ima Great MFT. That's I-M-A G-R-E-A-T. My number is 408-555-1234. That's 408-555-1234. I'm calling about my client Jack Klutz, K-L-U-T-Z, Plan ID# NCF0045672, SS# 167421861, birth date 2/1/61. He was authorized for 12 sessions with me, authorization number 4568473764, and he has only used 10. But I just realized the authorization expires tomorrow. I feel that medical necessity exists to continue treatment, including ongoing depression, anxiety, and sleep disturbance. I don't want to disrupt treatment. Is it possible to get an extension of the expiration date on this authorization until the July 31st? Thanks!"

▶ **A little self-promotion never hurt.** Always mention your name paired with the city where you practice. The plan representative may remember you next time he or she is looking for a referral in your area.

Tip: **Want to talk to a live person?** If you reach the insurance company's automated service (e.g. "for the status of a submitted claim, press 1, for claims address, press 2"), but would rather speak to someone with a pulse, you can often interrupt and say "Customer Service," "Representative," "Associate," or "Agent." Or, if all else fails, press "0" or say "Operator" -- even if these options are not mentioned. If this doesn't work, you can do nothing in response to prompts, and you will usually be transferred to a live person (they need to have this for those with rotary phones).

▶ **Don't take the "automated benefits" or "fax back" option.** The automated voice may offer to give you an automated (recorded) summary of benefits, or to fax you a summary of the client's benefits. Avoid this offer in favor of speaking to a live person. The answers you need are typically not covered in these summaries. Also, the summaries may have only information about medical coverage, not mental health, so they can be quite misleading.

▶ **Document the call.** Many insurance companies document all calls, and may even tape record them, which can be good for you if you later need proof they gave you incorrect information. But you should also document the name (first name and last initial) and the direct phone number or extension of each person you speak to, and a record of exactly what they told you.

▶ **Or forgo the phone altogether.** While I cannot more strongly recommend that you call when initially checking insurance benefits, a lot of follow-up information may be available via the insurance plan's website (ex. claim status, authorization confirmation, etc.), and you can often e-mail company staff to answer questions not addressed there. For more on what you can do at the company website, see Chapter 14.

7

Parity, HIPAA, and Health Care Reform
Legal Junk You Need to Know

❧ ☙

Just seeing the word "law" or "regulation" might make you break out in an itchy rash, and make you decide to skip this chapter. But don't. In the last few years there have been sweeping and historic insurance laws that are changing the way the whole system operates. Here are three important laws that therapists need to know about that may affect how you operate your practice -- and potentially help your clients.

Parity Laws

In 2010, federal parity legislation went into effect that was a true game-changer, improving the coverage of millions of clients, and bringing many changes for clients.

First, a little history. Historically, insurance covered medical illnesses only. When plans did start covering mental illness, clients seeking therapy typically had higher copayments and deductibles and more limited sessions for therapy, when compared to their medical visits. However, as evidence emerged for the biological basis of many mental illnesses, many states enacted regulations requiring insurance plans to provide coverage for mental illness that was "at parity with" (equal to) the coverage for medical diseases covered by the plan. This typically meant the same visit limits, deductibles, and copayments for mental health visits as for medical visits. But it is very patchwork: Some states have no state parity laws, in some parity is granted to all diagnoses, and in states parity is limited to certain diagnoses considered biologically-based (also called Severe Mental Illnesses, or SMI). Under California's state law, for example, only the following diagnoses are afforded parity coverage: Major Depressive Disorder, Bipolar Disorder, Schizoaffective Disorder, Schizophrenia, Bulimia Nervosa, Anorexia Disorder, Panic Disorder, Obsessive-Compulsive Disorder, Autism, Pervasive Developmental Disorders, and the Serious Emotional Disturbances of children (SED).

What changed in 2010? In 2010 the Mental Health Parity and Addiction Equity Act (MHPAEA) went into effect. This federal Act stated that health plans covered by this Act could no longer impose limits on inpatient or outpatient mental health visits if no such limit existed for medical visits. Plans could no longer have higher deductibles or copayments for mental health or substance abuse. In addition, if a plan reimbursed when a client went out of network for medical care, it also had to offer out-of-network coverage for mental health.

How did the Parity Act change things for my clients? The Parity Act affected over 100 million people in large group, state-regulated plans, and managed care Medicaid programs.

For most clients it gave them better insurance coverage for mental health and substance abuse. Most now were eligible for unlimited sessions, when before they may have previously been limited (there is a catch -- see below). Some clients now had a lower deductible and/or copayment. Some clients now had out-of-network coverage when they previously did not.

The fine print? The MHPAEA does not require a plan to cover all diagnoses, all therapists, or all licenses. And prior to 2014 the federal parity law will NOT apply to employers with fewer than 50 employees and to individual plans. And while starting in 2014, the Affordable Care Act required all plans purchased through State health exchanges to comply

with the requirements of the Parity Act, there are some "grandfathered" plans that were in place prior to this that don't have to abide by the MHPAEA. Also, the Parity Act doesn't require "good" coverage: A client may still have session limits, and/or a high deductible or copayment, if their medical coverage does.

And there's a bigger catch. <u>While most plans must now offer unlimited therapy sessions, they retain the right to cover only visits they consider "medically necessary,"</u> and this is fairly subjective criteria. Since the Act's passage, plans seem to be scrambling to figure out how to limit treatment using this loophole, and we can expect they will be looking for new ways to review (and possibly restrict) treatment utilizing their medical necessity criteria. Some plans have started to ask therapists – *even out-of-network therapists* -- to periodically undergo treatment reviews or complete written treatment updates to track treatment goals, progress, necessity, and effectiveness. For this reason, I strongly suggest all therapists (even those who never sign a plan contract) become versed in the language of medical necessity and get the plan's criteria (for more on Medical Necessity, see Page 48).

What if this Act doesn't cover my client? If you call the plan, and they tell you a client has a limited number of sessions per year, chances are the plan is not covered by the Parity Act. In this case, your state parity law may come into play. In many states (such as California, as was described earlier), equal coverage is limited to clients with certain diagnoses deemed "Severe Mental Illness (SMI) or "Biologically-Based" disorders. In these states there are two levels of coverage: one for clients who have one of the diagnoses listed in the state's parity law, and another level of coverage for clients with "non-parity diagnoses." Because states vary on which diagnosis are considered parity diagnoses, you will need to know your state's parity law so you can get accurate coverage information when checking a client's insurance. The insurance plan will not always volunteer information about this "higher" level of coverage that may come with a parity diagnosis. If the plan rep doesn't recognize the word "parity," try "Serious Mental Illness" (SMI), "Severe Emotional Disturbances" (SED), or "Biologically-Based disorders."

How can I find out more about parity laws in my state? Contact your professional association, your state's Department of Insurance (see Appendix A, Page 129), or the parity resources listed in the Resources List of this manual (see Resources, Page 133).

HIPAA: The Health Insurance Portability and Accountability Act

[Author's note: The following section is intended as a general overview of complex regulations -- I do not claim to be a HIPAA expert. There are many interpretations of this Act which will no doubt evolve over time with legal clarifications and challenges. For more information, refer to relevant citations in the Endnotes on Page 125 and the HIPAA section of Resources on Page 133.]

One of the most confusing issues for therapists is whether they need to comply with HIPAA, HIPAA, or the Health Insurance Portability and Accountability Act, was signed into law in 1996. The Act was passed in large part based on concerns about the privacy of medical information in light of the increasing use of computers by insurance plans and medical practices. It was also designed to streamline the electronic exchange of client information, to reduce fraud, and to minimize a client's chance of losing health insurance coverage when he or she is no longer covered by an employer's health plan.

HIPAA has four main parts that HIPAA providers need to become informed about:

1. **Privacy Standards:** Describes how a client's Private Health Information (PHI) may be used and disclosed
2. **Electronic Transaction and Code Set Standards:** Creates a universal "language" for reimbursement used by all insurance plans (ex. diagnosis and procedure codes).
3. **Security Standards:** Outlines how to safeguard confidential information from loss, theft, hacking, tampering, etc.
4. **National Identifier Requirement:** Requires all HIPAA providers to have a universal identification number, the National Provider Identifier (NPI), instead of using different provider numbers for each health plan (more about this on Page 36).

Do I have to deal with HIPAA regulations?

It's a good idea. But the Act states that only HIPAA "covered entities" are required to follow HIPAA's regulations. You are a covered entity if you are a health care provider, plan, billing service, or clearinghouse that conducts specific transactions via the internet. According to David Jensen, staff attorney at the California Association of Marriage and Family Therapists,

You **DO NOT** have to deal with HIPAA if you exchange all client health data with insurance plans by mail, phone, or fax -- not via e-mail or Internet. Common examples:

1. You have a private-pay only practice, and don't deal at all with insurance claims
2. You give invoices to clients to submit to insurance (see sample invoice Page 145)
3. You bill insurance, but ONLY submit paper claims by mail or fax and you have no one submitting electronically on your behalf (ex. a billing service or clearinghouse)

You **MUST** deal with HIPAA regulations if you exchange any client information with a health plan electronically (via e-mail or Internet), such as:

1. Submitting claims, inquiring about a claim, or receiving a response via internet
2. Inquiring about eligibility, coverage, or benefits, or receiving a response online
3. Requesting a treatment or referral authorization, or receiving a response online
4. Receiving an electronic Explanation of Benefits (EOB) or remittance advice online
5. Having a billing service or claims clearinghouse do any of the above on your behalf[16]

Questions and Answers

I contact clients via e-mail, or schedule appointments online. Am I a "covered entity?"

No. A client, acting on behalf of himself, communicating by e-mail, is not a covered entity, and is therefore not subject to HIPAA standards. HIPAA only applies when you disclose a client's private health information to a third party -- your client is not a third party.

Are interns, associates and trainees covered by HIPAA?

Yes, it applies to all health care providers, defined as "any person, business, or agency that furnishes bills or receives payment for health care in the normal course of their business."

What about notes? I hear HIPAA requires me to keep two different sets of notes.

Not so. Michael Griffin, staff attorney for the California Association of Marriage and Family Therapists, says "HIPAA speaks of two types of notes. The first type of notes is **progress notes**, which are part of the medical record. These are factual notes kept about the sessions (i.e. topics discussed, treatment plans, dates of service, and recommendations made."[17] Progress notes would also include medications, session start and stop times, the type of service provided, results of clinical tests, diagnoses, prognosis, and progress."

The second type is **psychotherapy notes** – an <u>optional</u> record you may keep of your feelings, thoughts, ideas, reactions, and analysis of sessions. HIPAA afforded these notes more protection – most notably from insurance plans. "Typically therapists should not have to release these to a third party, or to an insurance plan for an audit or evaluation. These should be kept separate from the progress notes, but some lawyers have interpreted HIPAA to say that you may keep these notes in the same chart as long as there is some divider. However, it may be wise to keep them in a separate folder," says Griffin.

OK, so if I'm a "covered entity," what do I need to do to comply with HIPAA?

It's probably easier than you think. While it is not within the scope of this manual to cover all the details of complying with HIPAA, here are a few things you'll need to do:

- ▶ **Learn about HIPAA and train your employees, if you have any.** I strongly suggest you attend a HIPAA compliance course or read a compliance manual.

- ▶ **Give all present and future clients a copy of the "Notice of Privacy Policies."** This Notice outlines HIPAA confidentiality rights and limitations. Clients have gotten used to receiving these from their doctors, dentists, and pharmacists. Many professional therapist organizations offer sample HIPAA Privacy Policies, or you can get one from any HIPAA course or manual. Do not alter the policies, just add your contact information, name, address, etc. <u>You will need to give a copy to ALL your clients from now on, even to private-pay clients</u>.

- ▶ **Have clients sign an acknowledgement saying they have received your Privacy Policies.** Again, a sample acknowledgement form may be available from your professional organization. Or you can do as I did -- I simply incorporated the necessary wording into the treatment agreement which I have all new clients sign (more about treatment agreements on Page 44; see sample treatment agreement Page 143). If the client refuses to sign the acknowledgement, document it.

▶ **If clients have objections** about HIPAA privacy policies, provide them with forms where they can express objections and ask for exceptions (again, these forms are available from professional organizations or any HIPAA course or manual).

▶ **Follow HIPAA security rules.** Provide computer security, including virus protection, backup, firewalls, and passwords. Shred old confidential records, lock file cabinets and offices, and limit access. If you want to exchange confidential client information by fax, you will need a dedicated fax machine (one that is not used also as a phone line) in an area that is not accessible by unauthorized persons.

▶ **Apply for a National Provider Identifier, or NPI.** The NPI is a single provider number that is unique to you, and used by all health care plans in their communication with you. Providers who are covered entities must use the NPI in all electronic transactions The NPI is free and easy to obtain. <u>The NPI does not replace the need to use your Tax I.D. number on claims -- either your Social Security Number (SSN) or Employer Identification Number (EIN) is still required for tax reporting purposes</u> (for more on the EIN, see Page 66, Box 25, or about getting an EIN or NPI, see Resources, Page 133).

While only HIPAA-covered-entities are required to get a NPI, <u>any health care provider may obtain a NPI</u> -- applying does not automatically make you a covered entity. However, soon NPIs will likely be mandatory. **Health plans are urging all providers to get one -- some are even requiring new providers to have one.**

Billing services and clearinghouses you work with should be instructed to use your NPI. Therapists who are employed by clinics or agencies should use the organization's NPI in one part of the claim, but may also need to get their own NPI for the box that requests "treating provider's NPI" (more about this in Chapter 11).

Is HIPAA being enforced?

Yes. Between April 2003 and January 2013 the U.S. Department of Health and Human Services Office for Civil Rights received over 91,000 complaints of HIPAA violations, where 22,000 led to various enforcement actions (from settlements to fines) and 521 were criminal actions referred to the Dept of Justice. The most common complaints were:
▶ Misuse and disclosures of a client's protected health information (PHI)
▶ No protection in place for health information
▶ Client unable to access their health information
▶ Using or disclosing more than the minimum necessary protected health information.
▶ No safeguards of electronic protected health information.[18]

A word about the "Minimum Necessary" standard: This HIPAA standard allows providers to use, disclose and request only that amount of a client's protected health information (PHI) that is reasonably necessary to accomplish the task. Providers have gotten in trouble by releasing/exchanging more information than necessary. In some situations you are allowed to release more than the minimum, such as when exchanging information with another provider for treatment purposes, when a client has signed a release, and when it is required by law, such as mandatory child, elder, or dependent adult abuse reporting.

For more information on HIPAA, and how to apply for a NPI, see Resources on Page 133.

Health Care Reform: The Affordable Care Act (ACA)

In March of 2010, President Obama signed the Patient Protection and Affordable Care Act into law, often referred to as "ACA," "health care reform," or "Obamacare." This Act set up a multi-year phase-in of sweeping changes in the health industry, will the goal of insuring all 33 million uninsured Americans, and making care more affordable.

Some highlights of ACA's provisions:

- ▶ **U.S. citizens and legal residents are required to obtain basic health insurance,** or pay a fee to help offset the costs of caring for uninsured Americans, (unless a member of an exempt religious group or waived due to financial hardship). The fee will go up yearly to encourage

- ▶ **Plans must now cover children up to age 26,** even if the children are married, live outside the home, or are financially independent

- ▶ **Medicaid income criteria was raised in many states,** allowing more to qualify

- ▶ **State-based "exchanges" (or marketplaces) were created,** through which individuals and small businesses can purchase coverage, often with the help of a government subsidy. Similar to travel websites which allow consumers to compare airline flight prices, the exchange shows consumers their insurance coverage choices, all in one online marketplace.

- ▶ **Exchange shoppers can choose from different coverage levels,** and different insurance plans providing the coverage.

- ▶ **Plans can no longer refuse to sell or renew policies to adults or children due to pre-existing health conditions, or charge higher premiums** due to health status (except for tobacco use)

- ▶ **Plans can no longer charge women more,** and can't discriminate based on sexual orientation

- ▶ **No annual or lifetime dollar limits are allowed on most covered benefits**

- ▶ **Plans now had to offer a minimum benefit package, including mental health and substance abuse coverage,** and certain free preventive services, including depression screening (and contraceptives, except for plans with religious exemptions)

- ▶ **Parity will extend to plans that are offered by (or absorbed into) the state exchanges** (for more on Parity, see Page 31)

- ▶ **Employers with more than 200 employees will be required to automatically enroll employees** into health insurance plans offered by the employer, though employees can opt out of the coverage.[19]

- ▶ **The ACA provides funding for more preventive based approaches,** as well as the creation of innovative and integrative (multi-disciplinary) care systems

The fine print: As this book goes to print (April 2014), it seems daily exceptions are made to this law, and I come across "grandfathered plans" that don't have to abide by the above rulings. There are many unknowns about what the ACA will look like once fully implemented, including how these new Exchange plans will affect those in traditional group or employer-based health plans, and how it will affect our clients and our practices. It is important to stay informed on this legislation. To get the most current information about Health Care Reform, see the resources listed in the back of this book (see Resources, Page 133), and stay tuned!

8

Starting Therapy
Checking Coverage and Intake Sessions

❧ ☙

You run a little victory lap around the sand tray when you learn your application has been accepted by CureQuick. Across town, Jack breaks down crying when he sees a pail in the men's room at work, and a coworker urges him to get help. He pulls out his tattered insurance card, calls CureQuick, and finds out he has mental health coverage as a member of their HMO plan.

First Contact

How does Jack come to be your client?

► **Jack gets your name.** How? Jack may find your name on CureQuick's website, where the CureQuick participating provider list is posted (note: be sure to keep your CureQuick profile updated once accepted). Or perhaps he gets your name from CureQuick, after calling them to request a therapy referral. Of course, Jack may also come to you via one of your normal referral sources (colleagues, former clients, friends, his physician, etc.).

► **Jack may then look you up on the internet.** Studies show between 75% and 96% of new clients search online when looking for a therapist. This means if they have a list of five names, and you have no website, clients are likely to go to the next name on the list. It is *essential* to have a dynamic, informative website that will attract potential clients.

► **Jack calls (or e-mails) for an appointment.** While you may do initial contact by e-mails, I like to talk briefly by phone before the first appointment (this reduces the likelihood of a no-show).

Also, I recommend that you ask <u>Jack for his insurance information during this phone call</u> (I'll explain why below.)

▶ **If pre-authorization (pre-treatment approval) is required**, Jack will need to notify CureQuick of the appointment and obtain an authorization number. Have him call you back with this number. <u>Most plans do not allow providers to bill clients for a session when the provider failed to obtain a required authorization</u>.

▶ **Just "passing through"?** Instead of needing pre-authorization, Jack may have a certain number of allotted "pass-through" sessions per year. This means that without talking to the insurance plan he can refer himself to therapy for a certain number of sessions. After this, you would need to contact the insurance company to get approval for further treatment. *Note: A client with unlimited sessions may still need authorization after a specified number of sessions, as the plan evaluates the medical necessity of treatment (for more on Medical Necessity, see page 58).*

▶ **Not a member of Jack's insurance plan? Don't despair!** Call the plan and check to see if he has coverage for out-of-network providers. In some cases Jack may only have a slightly higher out-of-pocket expense (e.g. a copayment of $50 instead of $30), and he may be willing to pay this difference if he wants to see you.

Why You Should Contact the Insurance Plan – Now

I can't stress enough how important it is to contact a client's insurance at the start of treatment. In fact, I typically do this <u>before</u> the first session. Many therapists do not check coverage, feeling (understandably) that it is the client's responsibility. It's tempting to let the client handle this, since it is time-consuming, and clients may appear knowledgeable about their benefits. But while it might be a hassle to check their benefits, if you don't you are increasing the possibility of claim denials, lengthy phone calls to investigate and fight the denial, clients upset by treatment disruptions, and therapy bills that clients may be unable to pay.

▶ **During your first phone contact with Jack,** after setting up an appointment, tell him you would like to check his insurance benefits to be sure there is no problem down the line. Clients are typically thrilled that you are willing to deal with their insurance on their behalf. Then get the necessary insurance information from Jack over the phone (see Page 41 for a form to use when checking coverage).

▶ **If you don't call now, you may not get paid.** If you don't check coverage up front, it may take months before you find out that your claim was denied, or that charges went toward the client's deductible. This could leave an unpaid balance of hundreds of dollar. Even if your contract allows you to bill Jack, he might be unable to pay, or he may have left your practice, making it hard to collect.

▶ **Find out if you need an authorization.** Several plans I work with do not allow you to bill the client for sessions where you failed to get needed authorization.

▶ **Don't assume.** You may think since you have other Pails "R" Us or CureQuick clients that you already know the coverage details. But every account may be different -- coverage depends on which CureQuick plan(s) Pails "R" Us bought for its employees, and which plan Jack chose. Also, plan benefits may change yearly.

▶ **Don't trust the information on Jack's insurance card.** Why not? See Page 45.

▶ **"But I don't have a release. Doesn't a call to Jack's insurance plan breach confidentiality?"** Some therapists worry because the client hasn't really even become a client or signed a release to allow this call. However, this type of communication is often permitted by law. For example, California Civil Code states that even without a release, medical information "may be disclosed to an insurer...or employee benefit plan...to the extent necessary to allow responsibility for payment to be determined and payment to be made."[20]

▶ **"But he already knows his coverage details."** Unfortunately, one of my cardinal rules is "don't believe anything your client tells you about his coverage." He is often misinformed or not aware of recent benefit changes. And after reading this manual you will know what questions to ask to determine whether your services will be covered, at what rate, and with what limitations.

▶ **"Can't I get coverage information by going online?"** Many plans have great websites that enable you to check benefits, deductibles, etc. But sometimes this information is incomplete or out of date, and may not answer important questions such as how much of a deductible has been used so far this year, or whether preauthorization is needed for mental health sessions. In addition, when you call, most plans document your call, which could help you to hold them accountable for misquoting benefits if you have reimbursement problems down the line.

▶ **"But I can never reach a live person!"** For tips on reaching a breathing human being and navigating the automated phone maze, see Page 28.

▶ **Call Jack back and clarify what his portion of the payment for the session will be.** Remind him to bring his insurance card to the session.

Again, all of this is recommended, not required. You may simply tell Jack that he must check his own benefits, and that he is responsible for paying whatever portion insurance does not cover, but it is hard to know how much to collect in the session. *And most of the therapists who consult with me after a claim denial could have avoided lost money and frustrating phone calls had they called and asked the right questions before treatment.*

Checking Benefits

On Page 41, there's a form you can use when you call to check coverage. A few notes:

▶ **"Behavioral health?"** Mental health benefits are also known as behavioral health benefits. Be sure to ask for <u>outpatient mental health</u> benefits -- the client's medical benefits may be different.

▶ **The insured vs: the client.** No matter who your client will be, you will need to get information about the insured. The insured is "subscriber" (policyholder) of the plan, usually the employee in an employer-sponsored plan. The client may be the insured if the policy is hers/his. If the client is using the insurance of a spouse, parent, or domestic partner, the spouse, parent, or partner is the insured.

▶ **Unlimited does not always mean unlimited.** Remember that a managed care company may not always authorize a client to use all their benefits. It will depend on many factors, especially whether they think there is a "medical necessity" for the sessions (for more about medical necessity, see Chapter 9).

▶ **Two insurance plans?** Always ask if a client is covered by two insurance plans (if so, see Chapter 17 for more on "double coverage").

▶ **Deductible used up?** Don't forget to ask how much of the client's deductible has been used up for the year. Jack may have a $500 deductible, but if he's already used it up for the year, you don't have to worry — just collect his co-insurance or copayment. If he hasn't used it, the first $500 of your charges will be out of his pocket. Remember that the deductible is shared with other health providers.

▶ **When do benefits renew?** While most plans operate on a calendar year, some operate on a 12 month calendar, starting July 1 or March 1, or other fiscal year time frames. Why does this matter to you? The deductible might start again mid-year, so the plan stops covering sessions while this is used up.

▶ **Don't ask if they cover couples or family therapy.** The plan may say no, when they actually do. They may think you are asking them if they cover non-medically necessary sessions focused on relationship issues and personal growth only. Ask instead if CPT code 90847 is covered for a client with a diagnosis. This is the code for a couples or family session from the American Medical Association's Current Procedural Terminology Manual[21] (for more on CPT codes see Page 64, Box 24D, and Resources, Page 133; for more on couples/family therapy, see Page 105).

▶ **Usual, Customary and Reasonable fees (UCR).** <u>This applies only to out-of-network providers</u>. UCR is the amount that the plan has determined is reasonable for the service, based on fees for similar providers in your area. Why should you ask about UCRs? It helps to determine exactly what your client will be reimbursed. Let's say your full fee is $120, which Jack pays up front. He knows he has a 50% co-insurance so he is counting on the reimbursement from the plan, which he thinks will be $60. But let's say CureQuick's UCR— the maximum they'll allow for this service – is $80. This means Jack will only be reimbursed for $40, which is 50% of the UCR. Plans won't always tell you their UCR (you may have to wait until the claim is processed), though sometimes if you tell them your fee first, they will.

▶ **Out-of-pocket maximum.** The insurance plan may quote Jack's "out-of-pocket maximum." This is the maximum amount he is required to pay "out of his pocket" before his insurance begins to pay 100 percent of covered expenses. However, since these numbers are typically quite high, in most cases this is not benefit information you will need to know, so I did not include it on the chart below, but it may come into play with your clients with chronic and serious illness.

▶ **Is the information I get a guarantee of coverage?** No. Be sure clients understand (and agree in writing) that they are responsible for any portion unpaid by the plan (see treatment agreements, Page 44, and sample agreement, Page 143).

CHECKING COVERAGE: 12 ESSENTIAL QUESTIONS

BEFORE CALLING INSURANCE: INFO TO GET FROM THE CLIENT / CARD

1. Client: _____ I.D. # : _____
2. Insured (if other): _____ I.D. #: _____
3. Relationship: _____ Group #: _____
4. Insured's Birthdate:____ /_____ /_____ Client Birthdate: _____ /____ /_____
5. Insured's Employer_____
6. Insurance Phone Number (*The card may say "MH/SA Benefits," "Eligibility and Benefits," For Pre-Authorization," "Customer Service"*): _____

THE CALL: WHAT TO ASK THE INSURANCE COMPANY

CALL DATE: _____ /_____ /_____ REPRESENTATIVE NAME_____

Request outpatient mental health benefits." Tell them if you're a network provider.

1. Copayment (flat fee) **or** **Coinsurance** (percent)	
2. Deductible (if applicable)	
3. Sessions Allowed per Year	
4. When Do Benefits Start & Renew?	Effective:____ /____ /____ Renew: ____ /____ /____
5. Deductible met so far this year	$_____._____
6. Is Pre-authorization Needed? *(for some plans, authorization is needed only after a certain number of sessions)*	No _____ Yes _____ **Needed After Visit #____** ▪ If Yes: Auth#:_____ ▪ # of Sessions Authorized:_____ ▪ Start:__ /___ /____ Expires:___/___ /____
7. Claim form: HCFA/CMS-1500?	Yes _____ No _____
8. Claims address <u>for EAP or MENTAL HEALTH claims</u>	
9. Is CPT code 90847 (couples / family therapy) **covered?**	Yes _____ No _____
10. Am I a network provider for this client's plan?	
OUT-OF-NETWORK PROVIDERS: **11. Is my license covered?**	Yes _____ No _____
12. Is my fee within the plan's UCR (Usual, Customary, Reasonable fee)? *have your most common CPT codes and your fees for each*	UCR: CPT CODE:_____ : $_____ CPT CODE:_____ : $_____ CPT CODE:_____ : $_____

Translating "Insurance-Speak"

Now for a quiz to see if you can interpret the language of insurance representatives!

For this example, let's say that you have signed a contract with Jack's insurance plan, CureQuick, to see their members at a fee of $67 per session. This is your "contracted rate."

WHAT THE REPRESENTATIVE TELLS YOU	WHAT JACK WILL HAVE TO PAY	WHAT INSURANCE WILL PAY
"He has a $10 copayment, after which he is covered at 100 percent of the contracted rate," or "he is covered at 100 percent with a $10 copayment."	Ignore the "100 percent" part of the sentence. Jack will pay **$10** (his copayment) per session.	**$57.** To calculate, take your contracted rate of $67, and subtract Jack's copayment of $10
"Jack is covered at 70 percent."	Since the plan is paying 70%, Jack must pay 30 percent of your contracted rate of $67, a total of **$20.10** per session.	**$46.90** (70 percent of the contracted rate of $67)
"Jack is covered at 90 percent, up to a maximum of $25 per session."	Don't waste your time figuring out what 90 percent of your contracted rate is. The rep is telling you that the most CureQuick will pay per session is $25. Jack pays the difference between the $25 insurance reimbursement and the contracted rate of $67, which is **$42.**	**$25**
"Jack has a deductible of $150, and none of it has been used. After that he is covered at 90 percent.	Here things get interesting. All of Sessions 1 and 2 will go toward the deductible, so Jack will pay $67 for each session, using up $134 of the deductible. In Session 3, Jack must pay $16 of your $67 fee to finish the deductible, plus 10 percent of the remaining $51 ($16 + $5.10 = $21.10). After this he will pay 10 percent of your contracted rate, or **$6.70** per session.	For Session 1 and 2, insurance pays $0. For Session 3, the plan pays $45.90 ($67 minus Jack's copay of $21.10). After this, the plan pays 90 percent of $67, or **$60.30** per session.

Care Denials: Bad News Before Treatment Begins

When you call to check Jack's coverage, CureQuick may tell you it does not cover the services Jack is seeking. Common reasons might be:

▶ **Jack is no longer (or not yet) covered by the health plan.** He may have recently left his job or started a new one. There is sometimes a gap between when a client gets a new job and when his insurance "kicks in." Another good reason for checking benefits at the start of treatment!

▶ **The service you intend to provide is not a covered benefit.** Not all insurance plans, for example, cover group therapy, extended sessions, parenting classes, meditation classes, etc. You may also be refused if it is not clear that a diagnosed mental disorder is being treated.

▶ **The plan doesn't cover "couples counseling."** Some plans don't cover couples counseling at all. However, most plans will cover couples sessions with both Jack and Jill, but typically only when used to address a diagnosable mental illness. To bill for couples therapy, you must be prepared to assert that one member of the couple has a diagnosis (typically a V-code alone is not enough). But remember: It is insurance fraud to overstate or create a diagnosis for the purpose of ensuring reimbursement. In addition, you may have to make the case that couples counseling is the most effective means to treat your client's diagnosis. (For more on couples counseling, see Chapter 17).

▶ **The plan is an "out-of-state" plan,** where the insurance was written for delivery in another state. This may be the case if the client is vacationing or temporarily working in your state, or if the employer's headquarters is in another state. In this case they do not have to abide by a state's "Freedom of Choice" laws, which allow clients a choice of providers with a wider variety of licenses. For example, I have seen instances where Blue Cross/Blue Shield of Florida has not covered visits to an out of state Blue Cross network Licensed Marriage and Family Therapist, since this license was not recognized by all their Florida plans. However, don't assume that because the insurance company has an out-of-state address that this will be a problem. Tip: Especially with Blue Cross/Blue Shield, ask what state the plan is from.

And what if you are denied? Don't be discouraged. Care denials can often be overturned if you know how to approach the relevant issues (see Chapter 13 for a wealth of ideas).

The First Session

In the first session, you might take some time to educate Jack about what it means if he chooses to use his insurance. After reading this manual, hopefully you'll be able to communicate with all your clients about the pros and cons of using insurance, and about confidentiality issues and coverage limitations, so they can make informed choices. Many professional organizations offer a brochure you can give clients on the use of insurance in therapy, or you may want to create your own.

If this is an EAP session, go over Jack's EAP benefit with him. Explain that your role is to assess his situation and determine if it can be resolved within the specified number of sessions or if longer-term counseling and/or a referral is needed. Also let him know about other free assistance that may be available to him via his EAP, such as legal and financial consultations, and referrals for child and elder care.

Reasons for a Treatment Agreement

I highly recommend that you give all new clients a treatment agreement. This agreement (which they will sign) is a form that educates them about how your practice operates, including your fees, the length of sessions, how payment and billing will be handled, the limits of confidentiality, your cancellation policy, termination, and after-hours coverage. It can also be used to inform clients about your insurance policies (see the Sample Treatment Agreement on Page 143). Some sentences that I have seen in providers' agreements to explain their policies include:

▶ *"The client is responsible for verifying and understanding the limits of his/her insurance coverage, as well as for any copayments and deductibles."*

▶ *"The client is responsible for any and all fees not reimbursed by the insurance plan."*

▶ *Either "the therapist is a contracted provider with the client's insurance plan, and has agreed to a specified fee, and will bill the plan on the client's behalf" or "the therapist is not a contracted provider with the client's insurance plan. Should the client choose to bill insurance, the therapist will provide the client with a statement of fees paid by the client, which may be submitted to the plan for reimbursement."*

▶ *"The client must pay all insurance copayments and deductibles, if applicable, at the time of the session."*

▶ *"If the client misses a session or cancels without 24-hour notice, he/she is responsible for paying the therapist's missed session fee of $ _____ (not just the insurance copayment). Insurance plans typically will not reimburse for missed sessions."*

▶ *"By signing this form, the client authorizes the release of any information needed to process insurance or EAP claims, to request additional sessions, to verify medical necessity of the sessions, or to satisfy the insurance plan's audits or quality reviews."*

▶ *"By signing below, the client authorizes insurance payments be made to the therapist"* (omit this if your clients will be paying you in full and billing insurance themselves).

▶ *"By signing below, you acknowledge receipt of the Notice of Privacy Practices, as required by HIPAA"* (Note: Include if you are a HIPAA "covered entity" – more on this in Chapter 7).

The Insurance Card – And Why You Shouldn't Trust It

PAILS "R" US

CureQuick
Behavioral Health   Wonderland HMO
www.curequick.com

GROUP: 23560   Deductible: $0
                               Office copayment: $10
MEMBER ID: PRU34567   Specialist: $25

JACK ISA KLUTZ

Plan 040: Wellquick Pharmacy – Medical

This card does not prove membership nor guarantee coverage. For verification of benefits, please call Customer Service.

Providers: For self service, go to www.curequick.com
Or call Customer Service: 1-800-555-3975

Claims: 12 HARVEY DRIVE, SUMMIT, N.J. 07901

For MH/SA benefits, call 1-800-555-5555

In the first session, copy both sides of Jack's insurance card, and keep a copy in his chart. Look for the phone number to call for mental health benefits. It might say "for Eligibility and Benefits" or simply "Customer Service." In Jack's case, you will see the back of his card has two phone numbers. The one you want is labeled "for MH/SA," which means "for mental health and substance abuse benefits."

So why shouldn't I trust insurance cards?

► **The copayment and deductible information may not apply to you.** The information printed on the front of the card may apply to medical services, not mental health, if the plan is not covered by parity laws. Or with a PPO it may say he has a $1000 deductible, but you might find out he has already used it up, or if he uses a network provider this is waived.

► **The claims address may not apply to you.** Often, the claims address is for medical claims, not mental health, and the mental health claims address is not even printed on the card. Do not assume the claims address is the same as CureQuick's corporate address, or the address where you mail other information.

► **Even the name of the insurance company on the card might be irrelevant.** Often mental health services have been "carved out." This means CureQuick may have hired another company to manage mental health benefits. Why is this important to you? A client may call and tell you she has benefits with CureQuick (for which you are a network provider), but later you find out her mental health benefits are handled by another plan, in which you are not a network provider. This is another reason to call the insurance plan before the client comes for the first session. Of course, this can work the other way: clients who tell me they have one plan (of which I am not a provider) may turn out to have mental health provided by another, so I will be covered.

The Perils of Private Pay: When a Client Doesn't Tell You About Coverage

After paying full fee out-of-pocket for three months, Jack surprises you by mentioning that he has CureQuick insurance, and asks you to bill the plan for past sessions. You are a CureQuick provider. Are you obligated to refund Jack for all monies paid for those three months, minus copayments and his deductible?

When a new client begins therapy and doesn't mention insurance, you may understandably assume he isn't covered. But he may be so distressed he forgets to mention it. He may have planned to come only for a few sessions, but as treatment costs mount he may look for ways to finance therapy. Or he may not have realized that his insurance covers therapy.

Is it really our responsibility to find out if clients have insurance? Well, no. But the bottom line is that it can blow up in your face if you don't ask up front, as in this scenario. If you are a plan provider, you agreed in your contract to charge all plan members only their copayment and any deductibles, and to bill the plan directly on the client's behalf. The only time you are relieved of this obligation is when a client has specifically asked you <u>not</u> to bill her insurance. From the standpoint of the insurance company, if a client wants to use his insurance, contracted providers need to accept it.

So what do you do now? Figure out what the client should have paid according to his coverage, refund the client the difference, and then bill the plan for the sessions. If your claims are denied due to "lack of authorization" or "late filing," file an appeal, explaining the situation, and ask the plan to reconsider their denial.

So what is the lesson? In the first session, ask ALL clients – even private-pay clients – if they have ANY medical insurance. If they have some insurance but you don't think you are covered, call and check -- <u>network affiliations can be complicated, so you may be a plan provider when you don't think you are.</u> Have all clients whose treatment is not covered by insurance (or who are choosing not to use it) sign a Private Pay Agreement, where the client attests that he does not have insurance coverage, or has insurance coverage but chooses not to use it, waiving reimbursement rights. (A sample Private Pay Agreement is on Page 149.)

9

Getting More Sessions
Authorizations and Medical Necessity

෨ ෬

So you've been working with Jack for some time, and of course he is improving under your expert care. However, while he is functioning better, he continues to have intrusive anxiety symptoms and sleep problems. He'd like to continue working with you, but you notice he is almost out of authorized sessions.

Managed care companies may periodically review treatment in order to monitor the effectiveness of the care you are providing. They are also assessing the clinical need ("medical necessity") for continued care (more on this later in the chapter). Since parity laws have done away with yearly session limits for most plans, more plans are reviewing treatment with an eye toward limiting it based on medical necessity criteria.

While any plan reserves the right to review treatment at any point, authorizations are more frequently required and treatment is typically more closely monitored for HMO clients. PPO clients don't usually require pre-authorization. And you won't usually request additional sessions with EAP clients, as the client usually is allotted the maximum number of sessions up front.

While some companies allow you to call to request more sessions, you may need to fill out a request form provided by the insurance company, sometimes called the Outpatient Treatment Report (OTR) or Request for Reauthorization (RFR). This form can often be filled out online at the company's website, or downloaded and faxed to the insurance plan. If approved, you will usually receive an authorization in the mail or by fax.

What will they ask? Using a checklist and/or a narrative format, the insurance company may ask your diagnosis, what symptoms the client is currently experiencing, why you feel there is a need for ongoing treatment, your treatment goals, and planned interventions for the next phase of therapy.

How often do I have to request more sessions, and what could trigger a review?

This depends on the insurance company and plan. Some plans allot the full amount of yearly sessions when the client first calls for treatment, so you shouldn't have to ask for more sessions all year. Susan Frager, a former case manager, writes that in some plans "case managers focus their efforts only on cases where the patient is not progressing, where utilization [number of visits] is higher than average, or on patients with chronic, severe conditions that need careful management to avoid multiple hospitalizations."[22] Meeting with a client more than once a week or for regular extended sessions might trigger a review. However, many health plans ask for a Treatment Update to be completed after a certain number of sessions (e.g the 12th session), and are scrutinizing care to see if the symptoms warrant treatment, or if therapy is simply desired by the client for personal growth.

What Case Managers Look For: "Medical Necessity"

Health insurance contracts are written for the purpose of covering sickness and illness. Therefore, the managed care company staff member who is reviewing your authorization request will be looking for the **"medical necessity"** of treatment. This means that he or she must be convinced that a psychiatric condition or illness is being treated, and that the treatment is medically necessary to treat the symptoms or illness.

What does this really mean? While medical necessity criteria vary between insurance plans, here are some common components that can give us a clue about what the folks at CureQuick might be looking for when they look over your request for sessions:

▶ **Medical symptoms and a diagnosis.** Jack must demonstrate symptoms consistent with a diagnosis from the American Medical Association's most recent ICD (*International Classification of Diseases*) or the American Psychiatric Association's DSM (*Diagnostic and Statistical Manual of Mental Disorders*).[23, 24] The two manuals share the same coding for psychiatric disorders, so when you are using the DSM codes, you are using the ICD codes. When listing a diagnosis, remember to use the <u>maximum</u> number of digits the diagnosis requires (3, 4, or 5 digits, depending on the diagnosis). The client usually needs more than uncomplicated grief or a phase of life problem (what was called a V-code under the DSM-IV). However, just because a client has a diagnosis doesn't mean that makes their treatment medically necessary in the eyes of the insurance plan.

▶ **Treatment must focus on reduction of these medical symptoms** (such as anxiety, depression, and insomnia). The primary focus of treatment cannot simply be personal growth, self-esteem, financial problems, career issues, inadequate communication skills, an annoying spouse, or parenting issues.

▶ **A decrease in functioning.** The symptoms are significant enough to have led to a decrease in functioning in at least one area as compared to Jack's pre-illness or baseline level of functioning. (Be able to articulate how).

▶ **The service is deemed appropriate** and within accepted standards of care for the symptoms, diagnosis, or treatment of Jack's condition. It is believed to be the most appropriate type, level, and length of treatment. And it isn't primarily for Jack's convenience (or yours).

▶ **There is an expectation that Jack has the capacity to make significant progress toward treatment goals** or that treatment is necessary to maintain the current level of functioning. At the very least, the plan must feel you are stabilizing the client enough to prevent hospitalization.

▶ **The client is engaged in treatment.** Jack must be motivated and participating in treatment, attending sessions and following recommendations.

▶ **The problem seems resolvable, and the treatment is working.** If CureQuick feels that it has paid for too much therapy without improvement, they may conclude Jack's problem cannot be resolved in outpatient therapy, or may need some alternative type of care. Clients who are not insight-oriented or have reached therapeutic plateaus may be considered more appropriate for referral to community support groups for maintenance. This places those with chronic conditions, including the severely mentally ill, in danger of eventual denial.

▶ **The client is receiving the right level of treatment given his level of functioning.** If you report a very low level of functioning, the plan may feel the client may belong in a higher level of treatment. If you report a high level of functioning, the plan may feel the client's treatment is no longer medically necessary, and that he could be referred to a community support.

▶ **They may want to see a treatment plan and discharge plan in place** -- documented in your chart or at least evident in your session notes -- which you have discussed with the client. Is it clear to you and the client what you are working on, how it will be worked on, how you will know when it is time to end treatment, and what supports will be in place at that point to prevent relapse?

▶ **When appropriate, the client has been referred for a medication evaluation.**

▶ **You've made reasonable attempts to coordinate care** with other treating providers, and documented it.

▶ **When working with a child or adolescent,** your treatment plan typically must include some family therapy, unless contraindicated.

▶ **It is believed the client could not achieve the same maintenance with medication and community resources alone.**

In addition, those evaluating your requests will check for potential risk issues, such as suicidal and homicidal ideation, chemical dependency, domestic violence, or abuse issues.

A Sample Narrative Treatment Update

Reading treatment reviews is time-consuming and costly to the managed care company. Therefore, the trend seems to be away from asking for a narrative summary of treatment. But in case you are asked to write a narrative summary with interventions and goals, here is an example that might give you some pointers:

**Progress Summary:** _Insomnia has decreased from daily to twice weekly. Nightmares and flashbacks of moderate intensity continue to occur twice weekly. While overall anxiety has decreased, client continues to experience phobic response when near pails, including heart racing, dizziness, waves of panic, a desire to flee, and nausea. Because his job involves frequent exposure to pails, he is on restricted duty, which has put a financial strain on family. He is irritable, has lost 20 lbs in 4 weeks, and has withdrawn from social interaction._

**Interventions:** _To reduce anxiety, use systematic desensitization, and teach anxiety coping skills, including relaxation, meditation, and visualization. Using Cognitive Behavioral Therapy, teach client to identify distorted cognitions that increase anxiety, using journaling, and written exercises from Anxiety Workbook. Recommend exercise, and assist in increasing social support system through support group referrals. Refer to Mindfulness-Based Stress Relaxation class. Give insomnia audiotapes to listen to nightly. Refer for medication evaluation if symptoms persist and monitor adherence to medication regime._

**Goals:** _Client will be able to return to work, and be able to be near a pail with no more than mild anxiety. Client will report less insomnia, and nightmares and flashbacks not more than twice monthly each, of milder severity and duration, which do not interfere with functioning. Periods of intense anxiety will be less frequent and of shorter duration. Client will demonstrate lower scores on Anxiety Checklist. Client will take any medications as prescribed, report practicing relaxation and coping techniques at least once daily, and use support system as needed to help him cope._

Authorization Requests: Dos and Don'ts

Do:

- ▶ **Focus on symptoms, and be specific.** Remember, this is the medical model, so communicate in this language. List the symptoms the client is experiencing that have led to a decrease in his or her usual level of functioning. Replace casual language such as "stressed" with specific clinical symptoms, severity and frequency, and scores on diagnostic tests. Include how the diagnosis has affected his "activities of daily living" (ADLs) such as work, family, friendships, finances, self-care, etc. Focus on current symptoms that support the diagnosis, and avoid irrelevant details.

- ▶ **Address how treatment will reduce impairment.** How will it reduce symptoms? And how do the sessions avoid the need for more intensive/expensive care? Remember, cost containment is one of the goals of a managed care company, so keep this in mind when conversing with case managers.

- ▶ **If asked about your goals,** make sure they are clear, measurable, realistic, and consistent with the presenting problem and diagnosis. Identify how you will know if the desired change has taken place. As in the narrative example above, try to quantify treatment goals. Don't focus goals on personal growth.

- ▶ **Explain your interventions** (what you plan to do in session or through homework to help the client achieve the goals). Again, see the example above. Avoid sentences such as "help Jack identify feelings about coworkers" in favor of more symptom-oriented and observable behaviors on your part.

► **Try to identify any areas of progress you see, however small.** Case managers understand that progress isn't always linear and smooth.

► **Document any referrals for medication evaluation.** With clients who have a major affective disorder, a referral for medications should be discussed with the client. Document this discussion, and referrals made, even if the client refuses to follow-up.

► **Document your referrals to community resources.** Document referrals to 12-Step programs, treatment facilities, classes or support groups, even if refused.

► **Document a safety plan** when the client is a danger to self or others or gravely disabled.

Don'ts

► **Don't be vague.** Case managers may remember the names of therapists who turn in poor treatment plans, those which lack specific goals and outcome or progress criteria. Vague treatment goals may lead to denials, or lead the care manager to authorize only one or two sessions while the therapist is asked to fill out a new treatment request or while they schedule a phone interview. More work for you.

► **Don't try to solve all the client's problems.** Identify goals that can realistically be achieved within a few months, if possible.

► **Avoid aiming for symptom elimination.** Remember that managed care companies may not feel they need to continue to cover a client until the symptoms have vanished. In some cases, returning the client to baseline functioning -- or stabilizing at an acceptable level of functioning and referring to community support -- may be all they will cover.

► **Avoid theoretical speculation.** Don't discuss merging, differentiation, attachment difficulties, projecting, or any theoretical buzzwords. Think medical and observable symptoms.

► **Don't dwell on the past.** Don't bring up the client's past, unless it is extremely relevant and directly impacts the client's present impairment. Even then, keep it brief. Stay focused on current symptoms.

► **Don't just list stressors.** Saying your client needs more sessions since he just filed for divorce does not give the case manager enough information to understand the symptoms that this particular client is experiencing.

► **Don't list identity problems or poor self-esteem a treatment focus.** "Saying a client has low self-esteem is the kiss of death," says former case manager Norman Hering. "Managed care companies don't see low self-esteem as 'medically necessary.'"[25]

► **Don't be afraid to say if the client is doing worse.** However, explain this, if possible, and identify any new problems that have come up since treatment began. Alter your treatment plan to reflect the new situation.

- ▶ **Don't reveal any more information than you must.** HIPAA requires that you make every effort to protect a client's confidential health information. In cases where you feel you need to disclose sensitive information in order to get more sessions, discuss this with the client (and document the conversation) so he can make an informed choice. He may decide he would rather pay out of pocket than reveal this information.

- ▶ **Don't just resubmit a copy of your last authorization request,** even if little has changed. The lack of new information may trigger a case manager's review.

It sometimes happens that your client no longer meets the criteria for medical necessity, yet you still feel the client needs ongoing care to address underlying or chronic issues. You may be concerned that these issues, if left untreated, could result in a regression of the client's symptoms. A client with a history of recurrent depression, a background of childhood abuse, or with perpetual problems with intimacy in relationships could fall into this category. If your client no longer meets the criteria for medical necessity, you have several choices: You can argue for the need for maintenance sessions to prevent relapse, request more sessions to do wrap-up and discharge planning, stop billing insurance and contract with the client to pay out of pocket, or refer the client.

Why Your Request Might Get a Closer Look

Let's look at some of the reasons why your request for more sessions might get a closer examination or outright denial:

- ▶ **It's incomplete, illegible, or too vague.**

- ▶ **It is a copy of the request you sent last time.**

- ▶ **You are ignoring a potential substance abuse issue.** You haven't assessed for this, or if you have diagnosed a drug or alcohol problem, you didn't discuss in your treatment plan the referral to a 12-step program or to treatment program for evaluation.

- ▶ **There is no medication evaluation.** This might happen if you have diagnosed Jack as having Major Depression or Bipolar Disorder, but he is not on medications, and you have not referred him for a medication evaluation or explained why you did not make such a referral.

- ▶ **You deferred the diagnosis.** You need to give a working diagnosis. You can always change it later as your assessment continues, if needed.

- ▶ **You did not include a complete diagnosis code, or any special modifiers (letters after CPT Code) that the plan may require.** As was mentioned earlier, it is important to add the full amount of digits found to the right of the decimal point in your chosen diagnosis code. The case manager may need to enter a full diagnosis into the computer. Remember that most – but not all -- diagnoses need two digits to the right of the decimal point (but some have one, others have none). Also some plans will ask you to add a modifier after the CPT code for EAP sessions.

▶ **If you're asking to see Jack several times a week, if you've used a lot of sessions, or if Jack seems highly impaired,** the case manager may question why Jack is not in a higher level of care. But don't be defensive. "Questions from the case manager regarding whether a client needs more intensive treatment are generally not a reflection of the case manager's opinion of the therapist's abilities," former case manager Susan Frager explains.[26] "Part of the case manager's job...is to consider whether another level of care would be more effective at helping the client reach the same treatment goals while conserving limited benefits."

▶ **Personality disorder.** If Jack has a personality disorder, it may be questioned whether he can benefit from ongoing insight-oriented therapy. Your treatment goals need to be especially realistic, and your case may undergo closer review.

▶ **You have a single case agreement with the plan, or your clients have complained.** In these situations, your treatment reports may get additional scrutiny. See page 25 for more on Single case Agreements.

▶ **No progress.** You've worked with Jack for some time with no improvement. The insurance company may consider discontinuing, or conclude that a different level or type of treatment is necessary.

▶ **Great progress.** If Jack's symptoms are mild and your report of his progress is too impressive, the insurance company may conclude that treatment is no longer medically necessary, and Jack is well enough to leave your care.

As you can see, treatment approval may require a client who is not too healthy, and not too ill!

Questions and Answers

What if Jack wants to use his insurance, but in our initial session it becomes clear to me that he does not meet the criteria for medical necessity?

Good question. You could explain to Jack that while he may be able to benefit from therapy, from what he has said thus far you do not have evidence that he has a mental illness that would be covered by his health insurance. You might also explain that it would be insurance fraud if you were to make up a diagnosis just so that he is covered, and that doing so could place your license in jeopardy. You might frame this as good news for him, as he will not have a diagnosis in his medical records that could cause problems for him down the line. You may want to call Jack's health plan to check if they will cover this initial assessment session, and if they might cover a V-code diagnosis, if he has one of these. You can offer to see him in your practice to work on his presenting problems, but be clear that he would need to pay out of his pocket, and have him sign a Private Pay Agreement (see Page 149). Another option would be to use a provisional diagnosis for a few sessions while you do a more thorough assessment, seeing if some diagnosis is indeed appropriate.

Let's say I have been treating Jack for many months, and he improves to the point that I no longer feel he meets the criteria for medical necessity. What then?

If you are merely wanting a few more sessions before ending with Jack to make sure he is stable and does not relapse, it could be argued that this is part of your medically necessary treatment to continue. However, if you are continuing merely because Jack likes coming, or if the focus of treatment is personal growth and <u>not</u> a mental illness, this is a different story. You could congratulate Jack on his progress, and explain to him you feel he has improved to the point that he no longer has a diagnosis that is covered by his health plan. While he might benefit from continued therapy, you would want to explain medical necessity criteria, and that he would need to pay for future sessions out of his pocket. Again, give him advance notice so that this discussion does not leave Jack feeling abandoned, and have him sign a Private Pay Agreement (Page 149).

Retro-authorizations and Extensions

> *"Yikes! "I just realized I've seen Jack thirteen times, and he only had an authorization for twelve sessions, which expired last week!"........ or*

> *"I saw my client three times, and I didn't know she needed pre-authorization!"......*

Being a managed care provider takes a bit of organization, and sometimes we overlook an important deadline. This may lead to sudden panic, and a certain amount of accompanying hair-pulling.

It used to be an easy thing to call the insurance plan and many would graciously or extend an authorization. Unfortunately, many insurance plans have gotten tougher about this, and in many cases they will not only deny your request but not allow you to bill clients for sessions for which you failed to get authorization. But don't automatically panic. Case managers get these calls daily. While it is possible that they might say they can't help you, in some cases they will "retro-authorize" these sessions, to cover a session that has already taken place. Many plans have a limit to how far back they can back-date an authorization, so call as soon as you notice.

What do you say when you call to talk to the case manager about this situation? See the sample script in the section on "Navigating the Automated Phone System," Page 28. Use a friendly but professional tone. Take responsibility for your error, but demonstrate that your primary concern is making sure your client's treatment is not affected due to your clerical error. Outline the medical necessity for any sessions that were not previously authorized (or occurred after the expiration date), and document the conversation.

If the case manager refuses, you can always appeal (a sample appeal letter requesting retro-authorization can be found on Page 84). You may need to call the clinical director or medical director, especially in cases where you are asking for a policy exception.

10
Ongoing Therapy

ℬ ℭ

So Jack has been coming to see you, and naturally, is progressing amazingly under your excellent treatment.

Feel free to pat yourself on the back! But here are a few things to keep in mind as you continue to work with him:

► **Be aware of your client's benefits.** While most plans now allow unlimited sessions, Jack's plan may limit the number of sessions per year. This may make a difference in how you space sessions.

► **If you have limited sessions, keep track of the number of authorized sessions remaining**, and the expiration date.

► **Deductible details.**   As was explained in Chapter 2, if you are a network provider and Jack has a deductible, you must collect your contracted rate (not your full fee) for each session until the deductible is satisfied. You still need to submit the bill to Jack's insurance (or, if you are an out of network provider, have Jack submit it) so that his payments will be counted toward his deductible; otherwise, the insurance company will not be aware that he has met his deductible.

► **New Year?** If Jack has a deductible, you'll typically need to collect it in the first sessions of the New Year. But don't assume you know how much it is. <u>When Jack's benefits renew, usually in January, call his insurance plan!</u> It's a hassle, but it's worth it to avoid later problems. Jack may have a new plan, or his plan may have a new benefit structure. Here's an all-too-common scenario: Jack is unaware his deductible has gone up from $500 to $1000, and his copayment increased from $10 to $25. By the time your January claims are processed and returned to you without a check, Jack may owe you hundreds of dollars. He may have discontinued therapy, making it harder to collect.

► **Document changes in diagnosis.** As treatment progresses you might reconsider your initial diagnosis, or the client's symptoms may change. Be sure to document your new or additional diagnosis (and the symptoms that led to it) in the client's chart, and change it on future claim forms.

▶ **Job changes may mean coverage changes.** If Jack leaves his job, be sure to check for insurance coverage loss or changes (see section below on "Losing Coverage").

▶ **Insurance authorizations are sometimes flexible.** As was suggested in the previous chapter, you can sometimes get case managers to extend the expiration date on an authorization if your client hasn't used all his allotted sessions. For example, if Jack has been given twelve sessions to see you, and has only used ten of those by the authorization's expiration date, it may only involve a simple phone call to have the insurance company to extend the expiration date.

▶ **Don't keep the doctor away.** Insurance plans want you to keep the primary care physician, psychiatrist, and all other treating health professionals in the loop. Get a signed release from your client. If he refuses, the refusal and reason should be documented in your notes. This is especially important if the client has a significant health issue, has substance abuse issues (or a history of addiction), or is taking psychiatric medications. Additional contact is recommended when the client is not progressing, unstable, at risk, or when there are significant changes in the client's condition.

▶ **If you need to refer Jack to another provider,** such as a doctor, a psychiatrist, a psychiatric hospital program or substance abuse treatment program, contact the insurance company (or look at the provider directory on the plan's website) for referrals within his plan. Remember that the client may need pre-authorization for this care, especially for inpatient or structured outpatient programs.

Losing Coverage

When a client goes through a major life change like divorce or the loss of a job, the possibility of losing health insurance coverage may be the last thing on his mind. But it should be on yours, as it could impact therapy.

If your client loses his employer-sponsored group coverage, in certain situations -- such as when a company changes health plans -- the new insurance plan may pay for you to have a certain number of transitional sessions with the client, to allow the client time to terminate or to transition to a provider in his new network (for more about Single Case Agreements or Transition of Care Agreements, see Page 25). You might consider using this time to apply to become a provider in the client's new health plan, or to explain to the client the option of contacting his employer's human resources department or benefit administrator to express concerns about the lack of continuity of care.

The client, of course, may choose to continue to see you, paying out of pocket. In this case, have him sign a private-pay agreement (such as the one on Page 149), documenting that he understands there has been a change in the payment agreement.

You might also ask your client if he is eligible for COBRA coverage. COBRA (Consolidated Omnibus Budget Reconciliation Act) is a federal statute that requires employers to offer employees and dependents who would otherwise lose their insurance the opportunity to purchase the same coverage the employer provides to its employees. COBRA is available for clients who lost coverage when they were fired, quit their jobs, had work hours cut to a level that they lost their eligibility for coverage, became disabled, divorced, lost their dependent child status, or when the employee died. If Jack lost his job at Pails "R" Us, and was in danger of losing his CureQuick coverage, he could apply for COBRA. This would entitle him to continue with the same coverage he had while employed, but he would take over payment of the premium (the monthly or yearly cost paid to receive the insurance coverage). No physical exam is required. But he must act fast to sign up so there is no break in coverage (breaks can jeopardize the ability to get later coverage). There are also limits to this continuation of coverage (usually 18 months for loss of employment or work hour reduction, 29 months for disability-related events, or 36 months for dependents who would lose coverage for reasons other than employment loss by the employee).

If your client switches to COBRA coverage, what does this mean for you? If the client submitted his COBRA application in a timely fashion and it was processed smoothly, nothing should change in your billing. You keep submitting claims, and the plan continues to pay, as if the client was still employed, since all that has changed is who is paying the premium.

If your client has exhausted COBRA benefits, he may then be eligible for HIPAA individual coverage an individual conversion coverage plan (offered by the same plan that provided the client's group coverage), or a plan offered by his state health exchange. For details about these plans and other health plans for clients in this position contact your state's Department of Insurance or Department of Managed Care (see Appendix A, Page 129) or see Resources, Page 133.

Questions and Answers

Will a case manager ever call to discuss a case?

Again, this depends on the insurance company, how much work you do with managed care, and the difficulty of the cases you happen to have. You may never be called. Even with my high insurance caseload, I am called by a case manager only about once a year. One insurance company representative told me that while her company had done away with the authorization request process, they still contact providers occasionally to check on progress in cases where you are regularly doing multiple sessions per week, or routinely doing extended sessions, or the amount of sessions had significantly exceeded what would be expected for the diagnosis.

Will the plan cover Eye Movement Desensitization Reprocessing (EMDR)?

This varies by insurance company. According to the EMDR International Association (EMDRIA) website, Aetna, Magellan, CIGNA, TRICARE, United Behavioral Health, and some Blue Cross/Blue Shield accounts are some of the insurance plans that may cover EMDR when medically necessary and when provided by a qualified behavioral-health provider to treat clients who meet the diagnosis of Post Traumatic Stress Disorder (CIGNA also allows it for Acute Stress Disorder).[27] However, plans may not cover it for other diagnoses, considering it experimental or unproven. If you run into difficulties, submitting research related to EMDR's effectiveness with your client's diagnosis can bolster your request. You will need to ask the plan if they cover EMDR, if preauthorization is necessary, if they cover extended sessions, and how to code them on the claim. One client I knew could not find an EMDR therapist on her health plan, and convinced her plan to negotiate a Single Case Agreement with an EMDR-trained therapist in her area (see Single Case Agreements, Page 25).

What if my client has used up all his sessions for the year? Is there any possibility I could get more if I felt it was absolutely necessary?

Thanks to parity laws, most plans now have unlimited sessions, but some still have annual limits. In these cases, you'd need to convince the plan to make an exception in this case. At times a case manager might approve a "trade" or "exchange of benefits." For example, if the client has 30 days of coverage per year for inpatient psychiatric hospitalization, the insurance company might be willing to trade some of those days (reducing the inpatient benefit) in exchange for additional days of outpatient therapy with you (increasing the outpatient benefit) in order to prevent a hospitalization. This is a cost savings for them – exchanging one day in a hospital for one hour of outpatient treatment.

What happens if a client complains about me to the health plan?

It is always in your best interest to take the pro-active approach and call the insurance company if you suspect a member is unhappy with you, before they call the plan. Take care to document these cases carefully in case a complaint is filed. If the member makes a complaint, you will be contacted for a response, a request may be made for copies of your records and other supporting documentation, and the situation will typically be reviewed by other clinicians at the health plan. The grievance procedure depends on the severity and type of accusation. But the emphasis is on improving quality of care and member service, not punishment, so most insurance plans will work with providers toward this end, whenever possible.

How should I handle a client who calls in an emergency?

Since emergency phone sessions are not typically covered by insurance plans (unless pre-authorized), you may want to schedule a face-to-face session as soon as possible. But therapists should not hesitate to tell clients to dial 911 or go directly to the emergency room if they believe the client is experiencing a life-threatening emergency. Most plans cover emergency services. In fact, some states have laws that forbid plans from denying payment for emergency services -- even if the situation is later discovered not to be an emergency -- if any prudent layperson would have considered it to be an emergency. Plans expect you to have some sort of emergency coverage, such as an answering service. In addition, outgoing messages on your office answering machine should direct clients to call 911 or go to the emergency room in an emergency, in case you are unable to be reached.

__Tip:__ When you write anything in a client's records, be aware that some insurance representative or another treating health professional may someday review it. Records should be in ink or typed, legible, dated, and in chronological order, giving symptoms, evidence for your diagnosis, referrals, and treatment plan. This is not just for your insurance clients -- this is just good sense for all your cases, to protect you in case of a lawsuit or ethical charge filed against you. Document any history of violence, risk factors, and use of cigarettes, alcohol, and drugs (illicit, prescription, and over-the-counter).

11

Getting Paid
Submitting Claims and Giving Invoices

ॐ ॐ

You've been working with Jack for a month, and you decide to submit claims to CureQuick.

Now, I know you are in this line of work because you care so much about humankind, but let's face it -- we've all got expenses to pay. So understanding the insurance billing and payment process is important. This is essential even if you never join a provider network, as in all likelihood you will be providing some type of invoice to many clients to submit to their insurance plan. So let's review the billing differences:

If You are a Network Provider:

▶ You should put your full fee on the claim form, not your contracted rate. An adjustment will be made by CureQuick before you are paid.

▶ You must take care of billing CureQuick on Jack's behalf. At the session, Jack pays only the copayment or co-insurance, and any deductible, if applicable.

▶ In your contract you agreed to accept CureQuick's rate as payment in full for your services. You can't "balance-bill," which means you can't charge Jack for the difference between your full fee and the discounted amount CureQuick pays you.

If You are an Out-of-Network Provider:

▶ If you have not signed a contract with the plan, Jack is a private pay client, and you can charge him your full fee. There is no discount, unless you are offering a sliding scale fee.

▶ If Jack wants to seek insurance reimbursement, you may give him an invoice/Superbill to submit to his insurance plan (see sample invoice, Page 145). A CMS-1500 form can also be used as an invoice for the plan.

Does being an out-of-network provider sound good now? Of course. But remember only network providers receive referrals from the plan, and Jack would not have come to you without this referral.

The CMS-1500 Claim Form (a.k.a. the HCFA-1500)

While a few insurance plans and many EAPs require their own claim form, the CMS-1500 is the standard claim form accepted by most plans. Distributed by the Center for Medicare and Medicaid Services (CMS), this form is often still called the HCFA-1500, its former name when the CMS was the Health Care Financing Administration. This form can be used by solo practitioners, groups, and facilities billing for outpatient services (if you are a facility billing for inpatient services or an intensive outpatient program, you may need to use a UB-92 form instead).

A sample of the CMS-1500 appears on the next page. Following that is a chart that gives line-by-line instructions and tips for filling out the form. A few notes:

▶ **Be sure you have the latest version of this form.** The latest version as of this writing (version 02/12) was required by most plans as of 4/1/14 for all dates of service. However, an older version of the form (08/05) is still floating around for purchase -- plans may deny a claim filed on this older version. You can tell you have the revised form if you see a black square "QR" code in the upper left hand corner of the form. If scanned by a smartphone's barcode reader or other barcode scanner, this code will take users to the website for the National Uniform Claim Commission (NUCC), where they can get more information about the form (for ideas where to buy the forms, see Resources, Page 133).

▶ **Can you handwrite these forms or make copies of a blank form and use that as a template?** It isn't recommended. For fastest processing, if you are not electronically submitting claims, health plans recommend that your claims should be:
   1. Submitted on the original red CMS-1500 forms (Medicare does not accept photocopies, and private plans may soon follow suit)
   2. Typed or computer-printed, using black ink, with block capital letters (no script)
   3. Free of crossed-out or typed-over mistakes (some plans suggest you use only lift-off correction tape to make corrections), and
   4. Neatly filled out, so that data does not overlap into other blocks.

   Why? Most plans have computer scanners that can only read typed characters on the original red forms. This means photocopied and/or handwritten claims will require hand-processing, which can significantly delay your payment and increase the likelihood of denial. In fact, according to Brad Lotterman of United Behavioral Health, "UBH receives more than 2,000 illegible handwritten claims a day."[28] Thus if you don't submit electronically, it may be worth purchasing the original red forms and a software program that allows you to print claims -- there are many inexpensive billing programs available (see Resources for where to get claims or billing programs, see Resources, Page 133).

▶ **Submit via mail, fax, or electronically?** Find out which the plan accepts – then it is up to you, but electronic billing typically leads to fastest payment (see Chapter 14 for more on electronic billing).

HEALTH INSURANCE CLAIM FORM

APPROVED BY NATIONAL UNIFORM CLAIM COMMITTEE (NUCC) 02/12

| | PICA | | | | | | | | PICA | |

1. MEDICARE (Medicare #) **MEDICAID** (Medicaid #) **TRICARE** (ID#/DoD#) **CHAMPVA** (Member ID#) **GROUP HEALTH PLAN** (ID#) [X] **FECA BLK LUNG** (ID#) **OTHER** (ID#)

1a. INSURED'S I.D. NUMBER (For Program in Item 1)
PRU3456700

2. PATIENT'S NAME (Last Name, First Name, Middle Initial)
KLUTZ, JACK

3. PATIENT'S BIRTH DATE MM 02 DD 01 YY 1961 **SEX** M [X] F

4. INSURED'S NAME (Last Name, First Name, Middle Initial)
KLUTZ, JACK

5. PATIENT'S ADDRESS (No., Street)
123 WATER STREET
CITY HILLTOWN STATE CA
ZIP CODE 95128 TELEPHONE (Include Area Code) (408) 5551234

6. PATIENT RELATIONSHIP TO INSURED
Self [X] Spouse Child Other

7. INSURED'S ADDRESS (No., Street)
123 WATER STREET
CITY HILLTOWN STATE CA
ZIP CODE 95128 TELEPHONE (Include Area Code) (408) 5551234

8. RESERVED FOR NUCC USE

9. OTHER INSURED'S NAME (Last Name, First Name, Middle Initial)

10. IS PATIENT'S CONDITION RELATED TO:

a. OTHER INSURED'S POLICY OR GROUP NUMBER

a. EMPLOYMENT? (Current or Previous) YES NO [X]

b. RESERVED FOR NUCC USE

b. AUTO ACCIDENT? YES NO [X] PLACE (State)

c. RESERVED FOR NUCC USE

c. OTHER ACCIDENT? YES NO [X]

d. INSURANCE PLAN NAME OR PROGRAM NAME

10d. CLAIM CODES (Designated by NUCC)

11. INSURED'S POLICY GROUP OR FECA NUMBER
H00123

a. INSURED'S DATE OF BIRTH MM 02 DD 01 YY 1961 SEX M [X] F

b. OTHER CLAIM ID (Designated by NUCC)
PAILS-R-US

c. INSURANCE PLAN NAME OR PROGRAM NAME
CUREQUICK HMO

d. IS THERE ANOTHER HEALTH BENEFIT PLAN? YES NO [X] If yes, complete items 9, 9a and 9d.

READ BACK OF FORM BEFORE COMPLETING & SIGNING THIS FORM.
12. PATIENT'S OR AUTHORIZED PERSON'S SIGNATURE I authorize the release of any medical or other information necessary to process this claim. I also request payment of government benefits either to myself or to the party who accepts assignment below.
SIGNED **SIGNATURE ON FILE** DATE 08 05 2014

13. INSURED'S OR AUTHORIZED PERSON'S SIGNATURE I authorize payment of medical benefits to the undersigned physician or supplier for services described below.
SIGNED **SIGNATURE ON FILE**

14. DATE OF CURRENT ILLNESS, INJURY, or PREGNANCY (LMP) MM 06 DD 01 YY 2014 QUAL. 431

15. OTHER DATE QUAL. MM DD YY

16. DATES PATIENT UNABLE TO WORK IN CURRENT OCCUPATION FROM MM DD YY TO MM DD YY

17. NAME OF REFERRING PROVIDER OR OTHER SOURCE
17a.
17b. NPI

18. HOSPITALIZATION DATES RELATED TO CURRENT SERVICES FROM MM DD YY TO MM DD YY

19. ADDITIONAL CLAIM INFORMATION (Designated by NUCC)

20. OUTSIDE LAB? YES NO [X] $ CHARGES

21. DIAGNOSIS OR NATURE OF ILLNESS OR INJURY. Relate A-L to service line below (24E) ICD Ind. 9
A. 309 81 B. 305 20 C. D.
E. F. G. H.
I. J. K.

22. RESUBMISSION CODE ORIGINAL REF. NO.

23. PRIOR AUTHORIZATION NUMBER

24. A. DATE(S) OF SERVICE From MM DD YY	To MM DD YY	B. PLACE OF SERVICE	C. EMG	D. PROCEDURES, SERVICES, OR SUPPLIES CPT/HCPCS	MODIFIER	E. DIAGNOSIS POINTER	F. $ CHARGES	G. DAYS OR UNITS	H. EPSDT Family Plan	I. ID. QUAL	J. RENDERING PROVIDER ID. #
07 01 14	07 01 14	11		90791		A	110 00	1		0B NPI	MFC27210 1386652212
07 08 14	07 08 14	11		90834		A	100 00	1		0B NPI	MFC27210 1386652212
07 20 14	07 20 14	11		90847		A B	110 00	1		0B NPI	MFC27210 1386652212
07 30 14	07 30 14	11		90834		A B	100 00	1		0B NPI	MFC27210 1386652212
										NPI	
										NPI	

25. FEDERAL TAX I.D. NUMBER SSN EIN [X]
261352705

26. PATIENT'S ACCOUNT NO.

27. ACCEPT ASSIGNMENT? (For govt. claims, see back) YES [X] NO

28. TOTAL CHARGE $ 420 00

29. AMOUNT PAID $

30. Rsvd for NUCC use

31. SIGNATURE OF PHYSICIAN OR SUPPLIER INCLUDING DEGREES OR CREDENTIALS (I certify that the statements on the reverse apply to this bill and are made a part thereof.)
BARBARA GRISWOLD, LMFT
SIGNED *Barbara C. Griswold LMFT* DATE 08 05 2014

32. SERVICE FACILITY LOCATION INFORMATION
OFFICE
4100 MOORPARK AVE SUITE 116
SAN JOSE CA 95117-1707
a. 1386652212 b. 0BMFC27210

33. BILLING PROVIDER INFO & PH. # (408) 0850846
BARBARA GRISWOLD, LMFT
4100 MOORPARK AVENUE SUITE 116
SAN JOSE CA 95117 1707
a. 1386652212 b. 0BMFC27210

NUCC Instruction Manual available at: www.nucc.org **PLEASE PRINT OR TYPE** APPROVED OMB-0938-1197 FORM 1500 (02-12)

WCMS-1500CS-12

CARRIER — PATIENT AND INSURED INFORMATION — PHYSICIAN OR SUPPLIER INFORMATION

Note: On each line of Box 24 Column J, use your NPI on white line. If you don't have a NPI, put license number preceded by "OB" on the shaded line above. **Do not use both as is seen here.** This is also true for Box 32 a/b and Box 33 a/b. *See page 65-66.*

Box	How to Compete the CMS-1500 Claim Form
Carrier Block	The "carrier block" is located in the upper right margin of the form. Enter the name and address of the insurance plan. Be sure to get the address for mental health claims (not always the same as the medical claim address on the back of the card). Enter in the following format: 1st Line – Name; 2nd Line – First line of address; 3rd Line – Second line of address (optional); 4th Line – City, State (2 characters) and ZIP code. The black square "QR" barcode on the left side of this block distinguishes this form from previous versions. The barcode can be scanned by smartphones and other code scanners, and will take you to www.nucc.org for more information about the form.
1	Identify the type of health plan with an "X". Mark only one box. Group health plans include those through an employer or group.
1A	Enter the ID number from the client's insurance card. Include any letter prefix -- omit dashes or spaces. Use the subscriber's Social Security Number if you have no ID number.
2	The client's full name. Last name first, then a comma, then first name (and middle initial, if known). No nicknames, titles (Mr., Capt., Dr.), or professional suffixes (e.g. PhD, MD). If the patient uses a last name suffix (e.g., Jr., Sr.) enter it after the last name, and before the first name. Do not write "SAME" in this or any other field, even if the information is the same as in Item 4; the plan may think the client's last name is "SAME." With couples or families, pick an identified client (s/he typically must have a non-V-code diagnosis).
3	Client's 6- or 8-digit birthdate. Put an "X" in box under "sex" to indicate male or female.
4	The insured's name goes here. The insured (or subscriber) is the primary holder of the insurance – the person whose insurance the client is using. This would typically be the employee in employer-provided plans. However, if the client has a unique Member Identification Number s/he would be considered to be the "insured." Last name first, then a comma, then first name. No nicknames, titles, or professional suffixes. If the patient uses a last name suffix (e.g., Jr., Sr.) enter it after the last name, and before the first name. Don't write "SAME," even if the information is the same as in Item 2.
5	Client's permanent mailing address (use two-letter state abbreviation) and phone number. Avoid P.O Boxes. Do not use punctuation or symbols in the address (except hyphen if entering 9-digit ZIP). Do not use a hyphen/space to separate digits of the phone number. Do not write "SAME," even if the information is the same as Item 7.
6	How is the client related to the insured? Put an "X" in the appropriate box. "Self" means insured is the client. "Spouse" includes qualified partners, as defined by the plan. "Child" is a dependent child, as defined by the plan. If the client is a dependent but has own unique Member Identification Number, report "Self."
7	Insured's permanent residence (use two-letter state abbreviation) and phone number. Avoid P.O Boxes. Do not use punctuation or other symbols in the address (except hyphen if entering 9-digit ZIP code). Do not use a hyphen/space to separate digits of phone number. Do not write "SAME," even if the information is the same as Item 5.
8	Leave blank.
9 A-D	Leave blank unless you answered "yes" to Item 11-d, and the client is covered by more than one insurance plan, or you are seeing a couple or family and you (or they) intend to bill two plans for the session. For more about "Double Coverage," see Page 106. In Box 9, enter information about the secondary plan. Enter the insured's last name, then a comma, then first name, comma, and middle initial. Then answer 9a and 9d as they apply to this person, leaving 9b and 9c blank. Do not use a hyphen/space within the policy or group number. Enter the name of the secondary plan, e.g. XYZ Insurance Plan.

10 A-C	Are symptoms related to a condition or injury that occurred on the job, or as a result of an auto accident or other accident? If so mark "yes," as there may be other applicable coverage that would be primary, such as automobile liability insurance. If there was an auto accident, report 2-letter state abbreviation where the accident occurred.
10 D	Leave blank, unless instructed otherwise by the insurance plan.
11	Fill in the group number from the insurance card. Do not use hyphens/spaces.
11 A-C	In 11A, enter the 6-digit or 8-digit birthdate of the insured person named in Box 4, and his/her gender. Leave 11B blank. For 11C identify the insurance plan name or type (e.g. "PPO Choice 100 Plan").
11 D	Check "yes" if the client, couple or family is covered by two insurance plans, and you (or your clients) have the intent to bill two plans (see instructions for Box 9, and "Double Coverage" on Page 106). If your response here is "yes," also complete Box 9 and 9a and 9d. Otherwise, check "no." This item is a required field. The provider here acknowledges having made a good faith effort to determine if there is other coverage.
12	Have the client sign and date at least once to authorize the release to the insurance plan of any medical information necessary to process the claims, and keep a copy for your files. Once you have the signature on file, you may write "Signature on File" on future claims. In lieu of signing the claim, the client may sign a separate release (same wording) which you can keep on file. Some therapists incorporate the wording from Box 12 into their treatment agreement and have the client sign and date that (see sample agreement, Page 143). If a separate release is obtained, write "Signature On File" in this box. Do not put any text in this box other than "Signature on File" or the client's signature. Parents/guardians should sign if the client is a minor.
13	If you want the plan to pay you, have the client sign here, or you may incorporate the wording from Box 13 into a treatment agreement or separate release and have the client sign and date that instead (see sample agreement, Page 143). If you do this, you may write "Signature On File" in this box. Parents/guardians should sign if the client is a minor. Leave this box blank if you want the plan to reimburse the client directly (i.e. if you using the claim form as an invoice for the client).
14	Fill in *estimated* 6-digit date the latest symptoms began. To the right of the date, note the word "Qual" and a vertical dashed line. Write "431" to the right of this line, which indicates this is the date symptoms began (doctors use another qualifier when recording Last Menstrual Period here). *Some plans will deny if you omit this qualifier.*
15	May leave blank. If client has had a similar condition before, give the 6-digit date when the client had a previous related condition.
16	Leave blank, unless the client is employed but unable to work. Give the 6-digit or 8-digit start and end dates of the time span the client is/was unable to work. If still unable to work, leave the end time blank.
17	You may leave blank, unless a doctor's referral is required for treatment. Enter first name, middle initial, last name and credentials of referring professional.
17A	Leave blank, unless a doctor's referral is required for treatment. If the referring physician has a National Provider Identifier, leave this box blank, and enter the doctor's NPI in Box 17b.
17B	Leave blank, unless a doctor's referral is required for treatment. Record the referring physician's National Provider Identifier.
18, 19, 20	Leave blank, unless otherwise instructed by insurance plan.

21	In the upper left hand corner of this box, you will see "ICD-Ind" and a vertical dashed line. This is where you will indicate to the plan what version of the American Medical Association's *International Classification of Diseases (ICD)* you are using to code your diagnosis of the client. Don't panic if you don't know what an ICD is – if you are using the latest version of the American Psychiatric Association's *Diagnostic and Statistical Manual* (DSM), the psychiatric codes are from the ICD (see Resources, Page 133). As of this writing, the switchover from ICD 9 to ICD 10 codes is scheduled for 10/1/2015, but the DSM 5 gives both sets of codes for each diagnosis. **If you are using the ICD 9 Code for the diagnosis, put a '9' before the vertical dashed line; if you are using the ICD 10 code, put a "0" before the vertical line** (see example pg. 61). In this box you may also enter up to 12 diagnoses in priority order. <u>A claim may be rejected if you do not use "the highest specificity" (i.e. the full number of possible digits)</u> for the diagnosis (e.g. if you write 296.3 instead of 296.33). <u>Most diagnoses need 5 digits, but some are only 3 or 4.</u> Use only codes -- do not write the diagnosis names. Do not defer the diagnosis, and avoid R/O (rule out). Choose the diagnosis you believe fits best – it can be changed or new diagnoses added. V-codes alone are not usually reimbursed. As seen on Page 61, if you add a diagnosis in the billing period, include both (or all) here.
22	You may leave blank.
23	Write the pre-certification or authorization number(s) here, if applicable. Do not enter spaces or hyphens within the number. If no authorization is needed, leave blank.
24 A	These six lines are divided, with a shaded portion on top and white portion beneath, intended to allow billing for up to six dates of service per page. Ignore the shaded portion of each line, and list session dates in the white portion of each line. For outpatient therapy, <u>list one date of service per line</u> -- you may either simply write the date in the "from" category and leave the "to" column blank, or repeat the date (ex. "01/06/13 to 01/06/13"). *Date fields should all be in either 6-digit or 8-digit format – it is recommended you be consistent throughout form.*
24 B	Enter the two-digit code from the Place-Of-Service Code list to indicate where the session took place. <u>Do not write "O," "OV" or "Office."</u> Don't use ditto marks or write "SAME" to indicate repeat information. The POS code is "11 for an office visit. *Codes may change, so go to "Resources" on Page 133 for where to get the latest Place of Service Codes.*
24 C	You may leave blank, unless directed otherwise.
24 D	Enter the American Medical Association's Current Procedural Terminology (CPT) code for your service, which identifies the type of service provided[29]. Authorizations may limit the codes you may bill for. Leave the "Modifier" column blank, unless instructed otherwise -- some plans use a modifier for EAP sessions. Do not use ditto marks in this section. ## *CPT codes frequently used by therapists in an office setting:* **90791:** Psychiatric diagnostic evaluation *(plans may cover only 1 per client, sometimes 2)* **90792:** Psychiatric diagnostic evaluation w/medical services *(plans may cover only 1 per client)* **90832:** Psychotherapy, 30 minutes *(for 16-37 minute sessions)* **90834:** Psychotherapy, 45 minutes *(for 38 – 52 minute sessions)* **90837:** Psychotherapy, 60 minutes *(for sessions over 53 minutes; may be seen as an extended session by some plans, require preauthorization, or may not be paid routinely -- see page 68)* **90846:** Family or couples psychotherapy, <u>without</u> patient present *(no time specified)* **90847:** Family or couples psychotherapy, with patient present *(no time specified)* **90853:** Group psychotherapy (other than of a multiple-family group) **90839:** Psychotherapy for crisis, first 60 minutes **90840:** Crisis code add-on code, each additional 30 minutes **90785:** Interactive complexity add-on code *(for more on this, see next page)* *(for more on this box, see next page)*

24 D cont.	*(continued from last page)* **A few notes:** • 90832, 90834, and 90837 may be used regardless of setting (e.g. office, home, hospital, etc). They may also include when a family member occasionally joins the client for part or all of a session, as long as the focus of treatment is the individual, and the client is present for some or all of the session. Use 90847 for ongoing couples or family therapy. • Add-on codes: List the service and charge as usual on the claim; on the next line repeat date and place of service code, then list the CPT code for the add-on code and any extra charge you choose for the increased complexity of the case • Examples of interactive complexity include when using play equipment with young children, interpreters or translators, when there is high conflict among participants or caregiver that complicates implementation of a treatment plan, or when there is a disclosure and report of abuse/neglect. This code can only be used with diagnostic evaluations, psychotherapy, or group codes, not couples/family therapy or crisis codes. • Codes do not vary by state or by plan. However, reimbursement rates for each code and which may be covered does vary by plan. ***For more on CPT coding, including for sessions over 52 minutes, see Questions, Page 68. For more on CPT Code information, see "Resources," Page 133.*** *CPT codes ©American Medical Association. All rights reserved.*[29]
24 E	For each date of service, go back to the letters listed before each diagnosis in Box 21, and note which you treated in that session. For example, if in session #1 you focused just on the first diagnosis you listed in Box 21, write "A" for that date of service). If you focused on more than one diagnosis in that session, enter the corresponding letters of the diagnoses, without commas between them (e.g., "AC" or "ABC"). As in the example on Page 61, if you add a diagnosis during the billing period, it may be reflected by an additional letter in this column. Don't use ditto marks to indicate duplicate information. Do not write out the name of the diagnosis focused on, or use diagnosis codes in this box.
24 F	Network providers: Write your normal fee (not the discounted contracted rate) for the listed service -- the plan will automatically adjust it. Out-of-network providers: write what was charged for the session. Do not use commas, periods, or dollar signs. Enter 00 in the cents area if a whole number. Don't use ditto marks.
24 G	Write number of units of service/sessions billed on that line (usually one). No ditto marks.
24 H	You may leave blank, unless otherwise indicated by the plan.
24 I – J	In Column J you will give the ID of the treating provider for each date of service. Column I tells which type of ID number you will be giving in Column J. <u>Note: In the sample claim on Page 61, it shows how to list your National Provider Identifier (NPI) and your non-NPI (also called your legacy number), but you should not list both.</u> **If you have a NPI,** write it in the white area of Column J next to "NPI" in Column I for each date of service (see sample on Page 61). Leave the shaded portion of each line blank. **If you DON'T have a NPI,** leave the white portion of each line of Column J blank. Choose another type of approved ID number ("legacy number") to use instead. While there are a number of choices, I recommend you use your State License Number. In this case, you would fill in the shaded half of Column I (above the letters "NPI") with the 2-digit prefix 0B, which is just a qualifier code that tells the plan that the next number that follows in Column J will be your license number. In Column J, enter your license number (including any letters e.g MFC27210) in the shaded area of each line. **If you bill electronically (via the internet) you must use a NPI.**

25	Claims must have the Tax ID Number (TIN) of the billing provider, even if you use a NPI or legacy number elsewhere on the form. Do not enter hyphens. There are two types of TINs: Social Security Number (SSN) or Employer Identification Number (EIN). I strongly recommend you get your EIN so you don't have to use your Social Security Number on claims, to prevent identity theft. The EIN is free and easy to obtain, and you can get one even if you have no other employees (see Resources on Page 133 for where to get it). My recommendation: Get your EIN before applying to insurance plans. If you have already been using your SSN, you will need to submit an IRS W-9 form to each plan, giving them your new EIN number. Contact health plans to be sure your EIN is on file and that your SSN is removed before submitting claims or payments may be denied. It is recommended that you make your EIN effective the beginning of a calendar year.
26	You may skip. If you assign clients an account number, you may record it here.
27	Enter an "X" in the "Yes" box. This indicates you are willing to accept payment under the terms of the insurance plan's program. If you mark "No" your claim may be rejected.
28	Add the total of all individual line charges on the page. Do not use commas, periods, or dollar signs. Enter 00 in the cents area if the amount is a whole number.
29	This is where you would normally report the amount received from the client. However, if you are a network provider, most plans don't need you to complete this section. The insurance company will calculate what it owes without this information, and it is up to you to collect any copayments or deductibles. If you are an out-of-network provider using this form as an invoice or to seek reimbursement, you must enter what clients have paid you. Do not use dollar signs, commas, or periods. Enter "00" in the cents column if the amount is a whole number.
30	You should leave blank.
31	Sign here, including degree, credentials, or license, and date. Do not use facility name. While interns or associates typically are not reimbursed by insurance, some plans do allow this. If you have the health plan's approval, the intern/associate and supervisor should both sign, and titles such as "treating therapist" and "supervising therapist" should be used to clearly indicate roles. If unlicensed, the word "Intern" or "Associate" should be spelled out. You may not give the appearance that the unlicensed person is licensed or that the supervisor performed the therapy. Enter either the 6-digit date, 8-digit date, or alphanumeric date (e.g., August 28, 2014). A signature may be replaced with a computer-generated signature.
32 & 32 A-B	Enter the name and address where the services were rendered, other than the client's home. No post office boxes are allowed. Use first line for name of practice or facility, second line for address, and third line for city, state, and 9-digit ZIP. Do not use punctuation or symbols in the address, except for a hyphen in 9-digit ZIP. **If the service location is your office,** use your NPI number in Box 32a (if you have one) and skip 32b. Remember if you bill electronically you must use a NPI. **If the service site is an agency,** use their NPI in 32a, and skip 32b. **If you or the agency does not have a NPI,** leave 32a blank, and in Box 32b give a non-NPI "legacy number." I recommend you simply use your state license number. Before your license number you'll need a 2-digit "qualifier" code prefix that identifies the type of non-NPI ID number you are using. For example, the qualifier prefix OB indicates that the next series of letters and numbers to follow are your state license, and might look like OBMFC27210). Important Note: In the sample claim on Page 61, I show examples of listing an NPI and non-NPI (legacy number) in this box. *You should only put one or the other, not both.*

	Print your name, or the name of the group or facility who is requesting to be paid for services. Include your degree or license, if applicable. Put your name (or the facility's) on the top line, address on second, and City, State and ZIP on bottom line. Do not use punctuation or symbols, except hyphens if you use a 9-digit ZIP. Your billing address is not always the same as the location where you provided the services. Enter your phone number in upper right portion of the box; do not use a hyphen or space as a separator within the phone number.
33 & 33	If the billing provider/facility has a National Provider Identifier (NPI), write it in Box 33a, and skip 33b. Remember if you bill electronically (via the Internet), an NPI must be used.
33 A-B	If the billing provider does not have a NPI, skip 33a, and in 33b give a non-NPI "legacy number." I recommend you simply use your state license number. Before your license number you'll need a 2-digit "qualifier" code prefix that identifies the type of non-NPI ID number you are using. For example, the qualifier prefix OB indicates that the next series of letters and numbers to follow are your state license, and might look like OBMFC27210). Don't use a hyphen or separator between the prefix and the legacy number. **Note:** <u>In the sample claim on Page 61, I show examples of both how to list your NPI and your non-NPI (legacy number) in this box.</u> <u>You only need one or the other.</u> If your client was seen at a facility or group, and they are billing for the service, use their NPI or non-NPI legacy number, not yours. Remember if you bill electronically an NPI must be used.

Adapted from instructions in the National Uniform Claim Committee's Claim Form Instruction Manual.[30]

A Few General Claims Tips

▶ **Record the date you submitted the claim** in a ledger, computer, or the client's chart (see sample Service Record on Page 147).

▶ **Keep a copy of all paper claims you submit.**

▶ **Fill out forms slowly, neatly, and carefully.** Proofread them before sending them. A simple oversight, mistake, or illegible entry could delay payment by weeks or lead to denial.

▶ **In certain situations, it is a good idea to submit a completed Coordination of Benefits (COB) form** with the first claim. This form was developed to help the client's plan find out if there is another coverage plan that might be primary or secondary. This coordination prevents a provider from collecting more than their full fee from two insurance plans, and prevents a secondary plan from paying first. For example, if Jack is employed, but you are submitting his claim to Jill's insurance plan, her plan might wonder why Jack's insurance plan isn't footing the bill. Without this form, CureQuick may pend (delay processing of) the claim until they receive it. In a case like this, where your client is employed but they don't have insurance through their employer, submitting a COB form with the first claim may be a good idea. The COB form is usually available from the insurance plan (you can download it from their website, or have them fax it to you). For more on "double coverage," see Page 106.

Questions and Answers

"I usually meet about 55 – 60 minutes with clients. Do I have to use the 45 minute CPT code, or can I use the 60 minute code regularly and get paid?'

It depends on the plan. This may be fine. But it also may backfire on you – you may be paid the same as for a 45 minute session, or you may not be paid at all. Read on to learn more.

I like to do 60 - 120 minute sessions with clients. Why is there only one CPT code for over 53 minutes?" Plans seem to be moving away from reimbursing longer sessions (and yes, 53 minutes is now considered by most plans as an "extended session"). They may only reimburse longer sessions with preauthorization, in special circumstances, or without preauthorization if not used too frequently. Different plans have different policies.

So you may want to use the 90837 code (for 60 minutes and above) carefully. In addition to this code, in a CPT Code Corrections Manual that came out after the 2013 CPT codes were published, the AMA stated that CPT codes 99354 (60 minutes Prolonged Services) and 99355 (Prolonged Services, each additional 30 minutes) could be used together for psychotherapy of 90 minutes or longer.[31] However, I would be VERY wary of using these codes without talking to the plans first – plans may choose not reimburse for these codes, or may reimburse only for physicians, as codes that begin with 99xxx typically have been reserved for medical providers.

What other coding options do you have? If the extended session meets the criteria for a crisis session, you might use the crisis codes (check if authorization is needed). If not a crisis session, explain to the plan why you feel the need for extended sessions, and if approved, how they want you to code it. Another option might be to bill one 45 or 60 minute session to insurance and contract privately with the client to pay any additional time out of pocket (have them agree to this in writing). However, says Kevin Petersen, a Network Consultant at Anthem Blue Cross, "I wouldn't recommend regular two hour sessions. Clients may agree to pay the difference but later file a grievance, even though they have no grounds. However, if this were to happen, Anthem would back the provider up."[32] For a 120 minute session, you probably wouldn't be reimbursed if you billed for two units of 60 minute sessions. For a 75 minute session, you probably won't be reimbursed for both a 45 minute session and also for a 30 minute session on the same day (for more about CPT Codes, see Resources, Page 133).

Will insurers pay for online therapy sessions?

Online therapy falls under the heading of telehealth, which involves providing treatment, education, and administration of services over a distance. While each state defines telehealth differently, it typically involves the application of both video and audio technologies in synchronous treatment delivery (some states include telephone in their definition). While insurance has traditionally not covered online services, a growing number of private insurance companies -- most notably Blue Cross and Blue Shield -- are now approving online counseling on a case-by-case basis, especially in situations where there are inadequate providers in the client's area, or when a client is unable to come to the therapist's office. E-mail conversations are not typically covered. Some employee assistance programs offer online support as part of a wellness or disease management program, and some insurance plans now cover online drug and alcohol counseling after inpatient care and online smoking-cessation support.

The growing coverage of online services is fueled by state law. As of this writing, nineteen states and the District of Columbia now require private insurance plans in the state to cover some telehealth services, and Arizona will join this list in January 2015.[33] Many more states have these laws in the works. Some require that the coverage be equal to what would be paid for an in-person visit. "Of course, the plan always retains the ability to rule that they feel the client could come to the office, or that the visit isn't medically necessary," says Marlene Mayheu, PhD, Executive Director of the TeleMental Health Institute[34]. There may be limitations on the settings in which the online service can be provided, which practitioners are eligible for reimbursement, and what types of counseling can be provided.

"Check your state laws, then call the plan to see if this is a covered service, what approval may be needed, and how to list the Place of Service code on the claim form," advises Mayheu. As for the CPT code? "You would use the same CPT code you would have used if you saw the client in person, followed by the modifier -GT," she says.

If the client is not covered, and has a Health Savings Account, he may be able to use his HSA balance to pay for online counseling. Otherwise, plans typically will allow you to bill a client for this service, if he has signed an agreement in advance to pay. Mayheu reminds us "if you want to do online counseling, be sure you get specialized training in the ethical, legal, clinical, and technological issues that make this work so different" (for Telehealth Resources, see Resources, Page 133).

Will insurance cover phone sessions, or can I bill the client directly?

We have all probably provided therapy on the phone, such as when a client was in an after-hours crisis, or when she was unable to come to your office due to illness, or problems with transportation or child-care. However, most insurance plans don't cover phone sessions. When I asked one case manager why her company did not pay for extended crisis-management calls, she said they felt that the fee they paid for sessions included any telephone calls made to (or on behalf of) the client outside the session. "You will have some clients that need a lot of phone time, some that require little or none," she explained. "The fee we pay is an average of both." Some plans take U.S. Behavioral Health Plan California's approach, stating they will reimburse for phone counseling only in situations "when clinically necessary and appropriate," but that all phone sessions must be pre-approved.[35] As with online therapy, approval may be more likely when the client cannot come to your office or there are a lack of providers in his area.

However, if you read the answer to the previous question about online therapy, you will see that more and more states are insisting that health plans cover sessions over the telephone when appropriate. See the advice given in the previous answer about checking state law, plan coverage, and coding advice (use the -GT modifier after your CPT code to indicate telehealth services were provided).

If my client pays me in full, what kind of bill do I give him so he can be reimbursed?

I'm assuming you are an out-of-network provider, since insurance plans require their network providers to bill the plan on the client's behalf. You have several choices on how to bill the plan.

The first is to give him a completed CMS-1500 form (leaving Box 13 blank and checking "No" in Box 27, and filling out Box 29 to reflect the amount they paid. Or you may give him your own personalized billing invoice/statement/superbill (a sample can be found on Page 145). On your invoice, be sure to include all the necessary information needed for reimbursement, including diagnosis, CPT codes, Place-of-Service codes, your NPI (if you have one) and your provider tax ID number (i.e. Social Security Number or Employer Identification Number). In other words, put on your invoice all the important information from the bottom half of the CMS-1500 form. When submitting an invoice, your client may need to attach it to a completed billing form from his insurance company (he might obtain this from his employer or health plan).

Along with your first bill as an out-of-network provider, it is a good idea to send an IRS W-9 form, downloadable from the Internal Revenue Service website (see Resources, Page 133). The W-9 is a way for plans to verify your Tax Identification Number, which they need for all providers. You should only need to submit a W-9 once to each plan, so you get into their computers. If you are concerned about giving out your Social Security Number, I suggest you get your free Employer ID number you can use instead of your Social Security Number on all invoices (For more on the EIN, see Page 66, Box 25, and Resources, Page 133).

I am not a network provider. But if my client can't afford my full fee, and has out-of-network benefits, can I collect his coinsurance, and bill the plan for the rest?

I've done it, but it can be risky. First, some plans refuse to pay out-of-network providers directly, and will cut the check only to a client, no matter what you have put on the claim form. Then it may be hard to get your client to pay you, especially if he has left therapy. Secondly, it may be hard to know how much to collect from the client, since the plan may not tell you up front what their reimbursement cap – or UCR – might be (for more on UCRs, see Page 40). Let's say your client has an out of network co-insurance of 50% and your fee is $150. You collect $75 and expect a $75 check from the plan. However, the plan may limit their out-of-network rate to $90 per session, so may only reimburse you 50% of this, or $45. Now you need to collect the $30 remainder from the client (it would be fraud to bill the plan $150 and not collect this). Again, the client may balk at this, or may be gone by this time.

What if my client is covered by two insurance plans?

Ah, now things get interesting. See "Double Coverage" in Chapter 17.

Do I have to fill out a new CMS-1500 form every time I bill?

No. Many therapists I know simply fill out most of the form after the first session, leaving the session dates, CPT codes, signature, date, and session-specific information blank. Then they use this as a reusable template. Each time they bill, they simply make a copy, fill in the new information, sign it, and submit it, keeping the original template for the next billing cycle. *However*, as was previously mentioned, if you are not doing electronic billing, insurance plans prefer bills to be on original red CMS-1500 claim forms (not downloaded or copied forms), and these original claims are usually paid much more quickly, since only these may be computer-scanned (for some ideas where to buy these forms, see Resources, Page 133).

What about no-shows or late-cancelled sessions? Can I bill insurance or the client?

Most insurance companies will not cover missed sessions. One exception may be if the managed care company contacted you to set up an urgent or emergency appointment -- the plan will sometimes reimburse you if that client does not show up. Contact the insurance plan or check your contract for their policy on missed sessions. As for EAPs, some pay for missed sessions, most don't. With some EAPs, the member may lose one free session for each no-show. One EAP plan I work with pays $25 for the first missed session only. If you do bill the plan for a missed session, clearly indicate that it was a missed or late-cancelled session on the claim form. <u>Don't make it look like a face-to-face therapy session took place -- this is insurance fraud.</u>

As to whether or not you can charge the client for the missed session, contracts vary on this issue. You may not be able to charge your client for these sessions, but typically you can, but you would only be able to charge your discounted contracted rate. Most insurance companies allow you to bill the client for these sessions only if the client has agreed in advance (and in writing) to pay for missed sessions. This can be easily accomplished by having a line devoted to this in your treatment agreement (see sample treatment agreement, Page 143).

Do all plans accept CMS-1500s?

No, but most do. Some plans, particularly employee assistance programs, may require that their own billing forms be used instead, so it's a good idea to ask.

My claim was denied because I was late submitting it. Can I bill the client?

If you are a network provider, there is a good chance the contract you signed won't allow this. If you are an out-of-network provider, you are always free to bill the client for unpaid amounts.

How often do I need to bill insurance?

This is up to you, but I would advise at least monthly. Also, it's wise to submit a claim after the first session, to find out early if there are any problems. Obviously, the more often you bill, the more frequently you get paid, and not billing often enough can also bring big headaches. I have seen cases where therapists allowed large balances to accumulate, only to face trouble when the insurance company didn't pay. Also, <u>many insurance plans have time limitations on claims -- some will not pay if they receive the bill more than 60 or 90 days after the date of service.</u> Read your contract.

My routine is to bill on the first of the month for all sessions in the previous month. I also check client charts monthly to see if I have been paid for all submitted claims. In January, I will call all my clients' plans (and bill after the first session that month), since many clients' benefits change January 1st and I want to be sure I find out quickly if there have been changes.

How long should I wait before I call the insurance plan if I haven't been paid?

Blue Cross suggests waiting 30 working days for PPO plans and 45 working days for HMO plans. Many plans offer the option of tracking claim status online. If they say they didn't receive it, they may ask you to resubmit the claim. You may consider asking them if you can fax it to expedite processing. Don't forget to document your call, who you spoke to, and what you were told. If you resubmit it via mail, attach a Post-It Note that says "second submission," and identify the date of first submission, so that if it is after the claim submission deadline the plan will still accept it.

Will the insurance plan reimburse me for the time I spend filling out paperwork?

I wish! This is VERY rare. If you do try to bill for paperwork time, use a report-writing or appropriate CPT code -- do not use a CPT code that might look like you provided therapy.

What if I make a mistake on a claim I've already sent?

You can call and ask how the insurance plan would like you to handle it. Generally you can just submit a corrected claim (a duplicate of the original claim you sent – without the mistake). Attach a note stating that it is a corrected claim and <u>identify the change you've made</u>, or it may be rejected as a "duplicate claim." Some plans have a form you can download and fill out called a Claim Action Request where you resubmit the claim and tell them what you want done with it.

Can I bill for sessions from two separate months, or two separate years (such as December of one year and January of the next) on one claim form?

It's no problem to bill for more than one month on one bill. However, divide charges from two separate calendar (or coverage) years into separate claims (e.g., one for December charges, one for January) instead of submitting a "split-year" claim.

Can I charge the client interest on overdue copayments or deductibles?

Many contracts forbid this. Some allow this if the client has agreed in advance (and in writing) to this policy. Read your contract or provider handbook, or contact the insurance company.

Can I submit a claim for EAP and non-EAP sessions on the same form?

As was mentioned in Chapter 3, many EAPs require their own claim form, so you may not be able to use the same form for both EAP and routine mental health sessions. Also, EAP claims may need to be sent to a different claims address than regular mental health claims, even if being processed by the same plan. But even if the insurance plan allows both types of sessions to be billed on CMS-1500 forms, it is wise to separate EAP and non-EAP claims on different forms. They may need to be processed separately, and combining them may confuse the plan and lead to inaccurate or delayed payment. Remember that some plans even have their own CPT codes for EAP sessions.

12

The Check Arrives — or Doesn't
Explanation of Benefits and Denials

❧ ☙

Weeks after submitting your claim for Jack's sessions, you practically kiss the mail carrier when you see his bag holds an envelope from CureQuick. Before you dance on your desk, take a moment to look more closely at the paperwork you've received.

Inside the envelope you find an Explanation of Benefits (EOB) like the one below. An EOB outlines how the claim was processed, shows any deductions made for copayments, co-insurance, or deductibles, and shows the final net payment (if any) to you or the client. If you requested reimbursement, and all has gone well, a check is attached. A copy of the EOB is also sent to the policy holder; this may not be the client. Below is a sample EOB. If you find it confusing, don't worry – on the next page we'll discuss it in detail.

CureQuick Behavioral Health
788 Paper Street Suite 118
Paper Trail, MN 55344
800-555-1234

EXPLANATION OF BENEFITS

ISSUE DATE	CHECK NUMBER
August 12, 2014	**0002795220**

Control Number   0010388563
Provider Tax ID   26-1352705
CUREQUICK VENDOR ID: 67750

BARBARA GRISWOLD, LMFT
4100 MOORPARK AVE. #116
SAN JOSE, CA 95117

Patient Name: KLUTZ, JACK   ID Number: PRU34567-00 Acct. Nbr: 90 Group: HOO123
Claim ID: 05222451522   Claim Received: 08/06/14   CUREQUICK BH AGREEMENT

Service Date	Procedure Code	Billed Amount	Not Allowed	Allowed Amount	Deductible	Co-insurance/ Copayment	Claims Payment
07/01/14	90791	110.00	35.00 / 01	75.00		15.00	60.00
07/08/14	90834	100.00	33.00 / 01	67.00		13.40	53.60
07/20/14	90847	110.00	35.00 / 01	75.00		15.00	60.00
07/30/14	90834	100.00	33.00 / 01	67.00		13.40	53.60
TOTALS:		**420.00**	**136.00**	**284.00**		**56.80**	**227.20**

01 – This is the amount in excess of the allowed expense for a participating provider. The member, therefore, is not responsible for this amount.

Understanding the EOB

Why did you get paid only $227.20 when you submitted a bill for $420? For the first session, $35 of your $110 fee was "not allowed" since in this example your contracted rate for an intake session (CPT code 90791) is $75. In our example, Jack's co-insurance (the percentage of the contracted rate that he is responsible to pay) is 20 percent, so he is responsible for 20 percent of your contracted rate of $75, or $15. CureQuick paid the rest (Note: many plans like CureQuick pay a higher reimbursement rate for an intake session).

For sessions two and four, $33 of your full fee was not allowed, since your contracted rate for an individual 45 minute session (CPT code 90834) is $67. Jack paid his co-insurance, which is 20 percent of $67, or $13.40. CureQuick paid the rest ($53.60).

You'll notice from the CPT code of the third session that it was a couples or family session. In this case, $75 is your contracted rate for a couples therapy session, so the $25 difference between this amount and your $100 fee was not allowed. Jack paid his 20 percent of your $75 contracted rate, or $15, and CureQuick paid the balance ($60). Note that not all therapists charge more – and not all plans pay more -- for a couples or family session.

There may be a code, such as the "01" Code in the "not allowed" column -- it is footnoted below the chart, reminding you why that amount was not allowed -- that as a plan provider you have discounted your rate, and that you can't collect this amount from the client. This would be "balance-billing," which is not allowed when you have a contract. You must accept your contracted rate as payment in full. The discount is Jack's incentive for choosing a CureQuick provider.

What to Do When You Get the EOB

- ▶ **If a check is attached, a little jig is always in order.**

- ▶ **Check it for accuracy.** Underpayments often go unnoticed. Be sure the right amount of provider discount, copayment and/or deductible was taken out, and that you have been paid the rest.

- ▶ **If it was an EAP session, be sure the claim was paid in full.** The insurance plan may have underpaid you, processing it as a normal mental health visit, taking out a copayment.

- ▶ **If the insurance company has overpaid you, call.** The insurance company may have paid more than it should have for a session, or paid for the same session twice. While it's tempting not to report an overpayment, if you don't sometimes the plan may recognize their mistake down the line and ask you for a refund – after you've already spent it. If you don't refund them, the owed amount may be taken out of future reimbursement checks for other plan clients. Remember also that it is insurance fraud to accept an overpayment, and could put your license in jeopardy. The plans often will send a written request for refund.

▶ **If you believe you've been underpaid, call.** You can sometimes get it cleared up quickly on the phone. As always, document the call and representatives name.

▶ **Different claims address?** Don't lose sleep if the insurance company address (usually in the upper left corner of the EOB) is different from the address where you mailed the claim. Claims are often received and paid at different locations.

▶ **Record insurance payments in Jack's chart,** noting the date paid, check number, and the dates of service each check covered (see sample Service Record, Page 147). Then place the EOB in the chart.

Questions and Answers

Jack has a $250 deductible. Why didn't any of this go toward the deductible?

One of Jack's other providers (or Jack) may have submitted claims earlier in the year that satisfied his deductible. Or the deductible may be waived if Jack sees a network provider. Where parity diagnoses come into play, the deductible may also be waived (see more about parity on Pages 31- 32).

How long does it take to be reimbursed?

It varies by health plan, and depends on how you submit the bill. In my experience it usually averages four to six weeks for the checks to roll in if you mail the claims, but only two to four weeks if submitted electronically or at the plan's website.

If you do not receive an EOB within six weeks, your claim (or payment) may have gone astray, so call the insurance plan. Many insurance companies allow you to check claim status any time of the day by automated phone service or at their provider website.

What if an EOB combines payments for several clients? How do I file this?

CureQuick may list payments for Jack and another CureQuick client on the same EOB. It is important not to file this form in either client's chart. This EOB lists the name and private health information of another client, whose confidentiality could be compromised if filed in Jack's chart, where the record could be viewed by Jack or a third party who has access to Jack's chart. You could try to separate the portions of the EOB that refer to each client, or redact any information about the other client, and file them in each client's chart. I have a separate set of folders where I keep these "multiple payment" EOBs, which I file by the insurance company name.

My client doesn't want her husband to know she is in therapy, but she is using his insurance. Will the EOB come addressed to him?

Unfortunately, yes. Copies of EOBs and treatment authorizations are usually mailed to the name and address on record for the primary subscriber (in this case, your client's husband). This is a problem that to my knowledge has not been addressed. Your client may want to call the insurance plan to see if there is anything they can do. She may reconsider whether she wants to use his insurance. Or she might want to try to beat him to the mailbox. Most importantly for you, it is a topic worth bringing up in therapy with her.

I'm an out-of-network provider, but I offered to collect my client's coinsurance only and submit the bill for him. But I didn't agree to any fee discount. Why didn't the insurance company pay my full fee?

The plan probably deducted any deductible, and then paid only their portion for out of network providers (often only 50 – 60%. But 50% of what? Remember, plans put a cap on what they will pay – often called the "Usual, Customary and Reasonable (UCR)" fee. This is the amount that the insurance company feels is reasonable for a particular service -- the maximum the plan will allow for the service given your degree, license and geographical area. The good news? As an out-of-network provider, you can (and should) now bill the client for any unpaid portion of your full fee-- it can be fraud to bill the plan for a fee that you do not attempt to collect. However, it can be risky to bill in this way as an out-of-network provider; for more about this, see Page 70.

I got an EOB with an interest payment. How come?

Plans may be required to pay interest to providers if they do not process claims in a timely fashion. An interest payment came to me from Value Options health plan, explaining "interest is due when claims are paid over 30 business days after the claim date of receipt. A claim paid more than 30 business days after receipt accrues 15 percent annual interest each day until the claim is paid. An additional amount of $10 per claim may be included if applicable penalty payment rules apply."[36]

Why Your Claim Might be Denied

Perhaps everything sounded fine when you checked coverage. But once you submit the claim, it is denied. When this happens, the Explanation of Benefits should list a reason. In my experience, the listed reason for denial is often not the reason it was actually denied (go figure). While you can't always trust the denial reason outlined on the EOB, it is sometimes accurate. A few reasons why your claim might be denied include:

► **Diagnosis issues.** You have given your client only a V-Code, when most plans require a non-V-code diagnosis (except for EAPs, which allow V-code diagnoses). Or perhaps you may not have used the full number of digits required for that diagnosis by the DSM or ICD. Most commonly, five digits (two to the right of the decimal) are required for diagnoses, though some diagnoses have only three or four digits total.

► **No authorization was found** in place for the date of the session you claimed. The client may not have gotten pre-authorization for the visits (some plans need this before the first session; others require it after a certain number of sessions each year). It is also possible that your authorization may have expired by the date of the session, or you may have already exceeded the number of allotted sessions.

► **CPT code issues.** You billed for a type of service other than the one(s) that were authorized, used a code they do not cover, or used a non-existent or old code (for CPT codes, see Resources, Page 133). Or you used a CPT code for an "extended session" (this may include the 60 minute psychotherapy code), without the necessary preauthorization for sessions beyond the 45 minute therapy code.

▶ **Wrong place-of-service code.** For example, under "Place of Service," you may have written "O," "OV," "OFF" or "Office" to stand for office, instead of the required "11" (for "office"). Or you may have used the wrong code, or one they will not reimburse for (see Resources, Page 133, for Place of Service Codes).

▶ **Telephone or online therapy sessions were billed** when this is not a covered benefit.

▶ **You are not a network provider,** and the plan doesn't reimburse for out-of-network providers (this would occur with HMOs or EPOs).

▶ **Missing EOB.** If you are billing the secondary health plan, you should have attached the EOB from the primary plan (see Double Coverage, Chapter 17).

▶ **Déjà vu.** You have previously billed for this date of service, and it is a duplicate claim.

▶ **The client has exceeded yearly benefits.** Since most plans now allow unlimited sessions, this is rare. However, for the plans that still have annual limits, this is an issue. If you feel the client is in need of more sessions, you may want to contact the plan to discuss options, or look into an exchange of benefits (see Page 58).

▶ **The claim was not submitted in a timely manner.** Some plans require the claim be submitted no more than 60 or 90 days after the date of service. If you were late, and if you are a contracted provider, don't try to collect from the client -- the plan will typically not allow you to bill the client for your error.

▶ **The claim was not submitted to the correct claims address.** Always check the claims address by calling the plan before submission! <u>Never trust the claim address on the health plan card, or even the one given by the automated phone service at the health plan, as it is often the address for medical claims only, out-of-date, or just plain wrong.</u>

▶ **You submitted the incorrect claim form or neglected to include the required documents.** The plan might not accept a CMS-1500 (especially EAPs, which often have forms of their own), or may require the latest version of the CMS-1500 and you submitted an older version. Some companies (EAPs especially) might require that you send along treatment summaries or closed case forms before they will pay.

▶ **The provider was an intern or associate, and the plan doesn't cover unlicensed providers.**

▶ **The claim was incomplete or illegible.**

▶ **The claim is being held, or "pended," awaiting further information** needed to process the claim. Frequently, a claim is pended awaiting information from the member about "coordination of benefits." This is when the plan wants to find out if the client is covered by another health plan that should be responsible for primary payment of the claim (for more on coordination of benefits, see Page 67, and "Double Coverage," Page 106).

▶ **The client's plan has a "pre-existing condition exclusion."** While the Affordable Care Act did away with this exclusion in most plans, a few grandfathered plans are still out there that allow this. A pre-existing condition is a health problem that existed before you applied for a health insurance policy or enrolled in a new health plan. "Insurance companies and health plans are concerned about their financial bottom line," writes Michael Bihari, M.D., a healthcare consultant.[37] "It's in their best interest, therefore, to exclude people with a pre-existing condition, impose a waiting period before coverage starts, or charge higher premiums and out-of-pocket expenses" for those with health problems. They may also deny all claims related to this medical problem for a certain period of time. "A pre-existing condition can be something as common and as serious as heart disease, high blood pressure, cancer, type 2 diabetes, and asthma — chronic health problems that affect a large portion of the population. Even if you have a relatively minor condition such as hay fever or a previous accidental injury, a health plan can deny coverage," says Bihari. For employer-provided coverage, the exclusion period is typically limited to 12 months, and only applies to conditions for which you sought treatment (or should have sought treatment) in the six months leading up to enrollment.

The good news? This exclusion will often be waived if the client can prove they had previous health coverage without a 63 day break right before enrolling (also known as "creditable coverage"). For example, "if you had at least a full year of health coverage at your previous job and you enrolled in your new health plan without a break of 63 days or more, your new health plan cannot subject you to the pre-existing condition exclusion," says Bihari.

What to Do if Your Claim is Denied

Breathe. Count to ten. Meditate. Perhaps a little yoga stretching. Then see Chapter 13 for ideas on what to do next.

13

Appeals
Fighting Denials

ॐ ☙

The Explanation of Benefits comes in the mail for your sessions with Jack. However, no matter how hard you shake the envelope, the expected reimbursement check does not fall out. Upon closer inspection of the EOB, you see the charges were denied. Or perhaps you have requested more sessions, and you receive a message from Jack's case manager saying she doesn't see why the treatment is medically necessary. What do you do?

The 10 Rules of Successful Telephone Appeals

1. **A phone call should be your first response.** It often allows for a better understanding of the reason for the denial, and speeds up the resolution.

2. **Have the client's chart in front of you.** Take time to review the case before calling. Have the client's date of birth, ID number, dates of service, and other information available.

3. **If the issue involves medical necessity, prepare!** You might want to review the plan's medical necessity guidelines (often part of the provider manual, which may be available on the plan's website), and Chapter 9 of this book. Jot down some notes about your treatment plan, the client's current symptoms, functioning, medications, progress in treatment, and treatment goals.

4. **Put aside at least 20 to 30 minutes for the phone call.** You may need to wait on hold, get transferred, and talk to several people at the health plan in some detail. You don't want to hang up frustrated with the matter unresolved, only to have to call again.

5. **Take a deep breath.** Use one of those relaxation techniques you teach your clients, and get into your "happy place."

6. **Be friendly, stay calm, and avoid defensiveness.** Remember: The plan's employees are not your enemy. They are just doing their job.

7. **Be specific about what you want.** Don't whine about the health plan or managed care as a whole. While I'm sure whatever you are upset about is *completely* valid, the wrong attitude can quickly alienate those who are in a position to help you.

8. **When talking to a case manager, speak to her as a peer, which may be the case.** An increasing number of case managers are licensed clinicians. Assume that the case manager simply knows less about the client's situation than you do, and with some additional enlightenment, she might share your view.

9. **Avoid anything that might be interpreted as a threat,** or overly dramatic predictions that your client will decompensate or commit suicide if your appeal is not granted.

10. **As always, keep a communication log, and get call confirmation numbers.** Record the names of all those you speak with, dates and times of conversations, what they say, and call confirmation numbers. If they have agreed to resubmit a claim for reprocessing, ask them to read what they have written to the claims department about why you are requesting an adjustment, to check for accuracy.

Steps to Appealing a Denial

▶ **Call the health plan. But who do you talk to?**

1. **Claims issues:** Call the Claims Department or Customer Service. With your help, they often quickly identify their errors on the phone, and promise to resubmit the claims for reprocessing. At other times, they help you identify *your* error, and you can resubmit the claim. Be sure to attach a note (a Post-It note will do) clearly indicating that this is a "corrected claim" and identifying the correction so the claims reviewer doesn't miss the correction and deny it again.

2. **Treatment, authorization, or medical necessity issues:** Call the case management department -- you may need to set up a telephone interview with a care manager. Take time before you pick up the phone to put together a reasoned, clinical, non-defensive argument for why you believe the services are medically necessary (see Chapter 9 for more on this important concept). Key concepts: Be sure the treatment is alleviating medical symptoms (like anxiety, insomnia, depression) and be able to discuss how treatment has shown to be effective, and why you feel your treatment type and frequency is the best treatment alternative at this time for this client. Articulate how the sessions might help prevent a need for more lengthy and/or intensive (and costly) treatment such as hospitalization.

▶ **If you have to leave a message,** leave as much identifying information as possible. This may include your name -- spelled out slowly -- your area code and phone number (repeated once), the client's name -- spelled out slowly -- and date of birth, the policyholder's name and ID number, and date of birth (if client is not the policyholder), and details about your problem (See Page 28 - 29 for tips and a sample script). If it is a claims issue, include the date(s) of service in question, the amount you charged, and the claim number, if you have it.

▶ **If necessary, ask to speak to a supervisor.** Supervisors may have the power to make exceptions to company policy, or may be more knowledgeable about plans or parity laws. They may also assist if you have a complaint about a plan representative. However, you may not be able to bypass the claims or customer service representative or case manager; usually a supervisor will not speak with you unless you have discussed the issues first with someone lower on the hierarchy.

▶ **Ask for a phone appointment to speak to the plan's medical director or clinical director.** If you have spoken to the case manager and supervisor and have been unable to resolve a treatment disagreement, you may choose this option. When I spoke to a medical director it was a very positive conversation. He had the power to overrule the case manager's decision, and my request was fulfilled.

▶ **After talking to your client, submit a written appeal.** If you cannot get the matter resolved by phone, you or your client may use the health plan's formal appeal or dispute resolution process. This is a written notice to the health plan formally challenging a treatment denial or requesting reconsideration of a claim that was denied or adjusted. You may also use this process to ask for an exception to the insurance plan's policies. **A sample appeal letter can be found on Page 84.** Treatment appeals are then reviewed at the health plan by another clinician, a plan psychiatrist, and/or the plan's appeals committee. You may ask for an expedited appeal if you need immediate approval to continue necessary treatment.

If this is in reference to a denied claim, a letter outlining the plan's appeal and dispute procedure should have come with the denied claim. Contact the insurance plan for more details about its appeal process, what to include in your letter, and where to submit it. Be sure to file your appeal in a timely fashion. Most insurance companies require that you submit it within a certain time period (e.g., 60 days) of the denial. Many plans have appeal forms and instructions on their websites.

As always, focus on why the treatment is the most clinically effective and cost-effective. Include a copy of the EOB or any relevant clinical information and documentation with your request for reconsideration. Your client may have the right to receive, upon written request and for free, information the insurance plan used to review the initial claim or treatment request. This information can assist in an appeal. Revisit Chapter 9 for ideas to help with this letter if the denial involved medical necessity. You may want to hire an insurance consultant to help you craft a persuasive appeal letter (see Resources, Page 133).

▶ **Contact your professional organization.** They can often give you advice on how to challenge a denial, or which section of law to cite when appealing.

▶ **Contact your state's Department of Insurance** (and/or the state's Department of Managed Health Care, if you have one in your state -- see Appendix A, Page 129). Most states allow you to file a complaint (or appeal a decision by an insurance plan) after your complaint has been through the plan's internal dispute resolution process, or if you have not received a timely response to your complaint.

In addition, when a health plan is denying, delaying, or modifying a service because it does not believe the service is medically necessary, or they feel it is experimental, you may be able to request an Independent Medical Review (IMR) from your state's Insurance Department or Managed Care Department. The case is reviewed by experts in the field who are not affiliated with the client's health care plan. You can use this process even if you are an out-of network provider. Best of all, IMRs often overturn plan decisions; Of the medical necessity IMRs performed by the

California Department of Managed Health Care in 2010, 50 percent overturned the ruling of the health plan, requiring the disputed health care service to be covered.[38] You may be able to request an expedited review of the grievance for cases that involve an imminent and serious threat to the health of the client if treatment is disrupted. In extreme cases, it may be wise to file grievances with the plan and the state agency at the same time.

What will the IMR reviewers look for? It may be right on their website. The DMHC says "a review of a medical necessity case determines whether or not the disputed service is medically necessary based on: 1) the specific medical needs of the enrollee and 2) any of the following: peer-reviewed scientific and medical evidence regarding the effectiveness of the disputed service; nationally recognized professional standards; expert opinion; generally accepted standards of medical practice; or treatments that are likely to provide a benefit to a patient for conditions for which other treatments are not clinically efficacious."[39] (For more on Medical Necessity, see Chapter 9).

▶ **The client may get the employer's benefits manager involved**, asking them to contact the plan on the client's behalf, but it can be highly effective. Only a client should initiate contact with a benefits manager. Once when I was unable to get a denial overturned, my client went to the benefits manager at his company, who was able to get the plan to pay me. Because the employer pays the premiums, the employer often has more clout at the plan, and can be an influential ally for you. While cost containment is important to healthcare organizations, employer satisfaction is vital to their survival. They know that if clients complain about their health plan to their employer, the employer may find a new plan.

▶ **You or your client may have the right to bring a civil action** if a final appeal is denied. Consulting an attorney may be advised.

▶ **If the service will not be covered,** the client may choose to pay you out of pocket. It is wise to have the client sign and return a private-pay agreement (see sample on Page 149), stating that the client understands that he or she is obligated to pay for the services to be rendered, and that reimbursement was denied by the plan. This agreement should be given to the client in advance of providing the out-of-pocket services.

Specific Appeal Situations

1. **If you are not being covered because you are not an HMO or EPO network provider,** you or the client may write a letter to the health plan (perhaps with supporting documents from you and/or his doctor) that states the reasons he went to an out-of-network provider, and the reasons it is believed you are the best provider to see. Insurance may pay for out-of-network services when a case can be made that you have qualifications that network providers within a reasonable proximity do not possess (see "Single Case Agreements," Page 25). They may even pay your full fee (the plan may not cover sessions that have already taken place).

2. **If the service you provided (or intend to provide) is not a covered service,** be prepared to defend why the plan should make an exception in this case. Focus on cost-efficiency and most effective symptom-reduction. See Chapter 9 for ideas.

3. **If they say your license is not covered,** contact your professional organization, and appeal. The Affordable Care Act has made it so that most non-grandfathered plans "cannot discriminate with respect to participation ... or coverage against any health care provider who is acting within the scope of that provider's license or certification under applicable State law."[40] Also, many state laws forbid such discrimination. For example, California Insurance Code's "Freedom of Choice" laws (Section 10176 and 10176.7) mandate that insurance plans may not prohibit their members from selecting licensed Marriage and Family Therapists (and other named mental health professionals), even if the insurance coverage is provided by an out-of-state plan. However, there are exceptions.

4. **If the plan is not covered by the federal Parity Act, and you believe there was a claims error which involved parity** (i.e., your client has a parity diagnosis, but the plan processed it at a non-parity rate), remind the company of the parity coverage benefit. If the plan representative you speak with doesn't recognize the concept of "parity," s/he may recognize the phrase "Severe Mental Illness" (SMI), "Severe Emotional Disturbance" (SED), or "Biologically-Based Disorder." If all else fails, ask to speak to a supervisor, who may be more familiar with parity. Remember, however, that that some states have no state parity laws.

5. **If you are told couples counseling is not covered,** see "Care Denials," Page 43.

6. **If the insurance company told you when you first called that the client was eligible, or covered at a certain rate, but now say different:** Jack's employer may not have informed the plan about a change in Jack's employment status or coverage. Or the plan hadn't updated their info. Or the representative you spoke with gave you incorrect information. Don't despair! On more than one occasion I have persuaded plans to pay -- even when a client wasn't eligible -- when I was able to prove the insurance plan told me the client was eligible in the initial call. I had good notes from those calls, including names, when I called, and what was said. I argued that treatment decisions were based on that information in good faith. The claims supervisor pulled up the client's file and viewed the call notes, enabling her to see it had been the representative's mistake. Now you can't count on this, as most health plans give a disclaimer on the phone that says that quoted benefits are not guaranteed, and coverage cannot be determined until you submit a claim.

7. **If the plan paid for a period of time, then discontinued payment or demands reimbursement,** call the plan. Sometimes in your appeal you can use a theory of common law known as estoppel. Since the plan has paid for a period of time, and since the insurance company was responsible for determining the terms and conditions of the contract, you might argue that by their reimbursement you had every reason to believe they would continue to pay, and you and your client relied on this to make treatment decisions. Thus the company is estopped, or barred, from discontinuing treatment once it has made such a "ruling" on the coverage.[41]

Sample Appeal Letter

Barbara Griswold, LMFT
4100 Moorpark Ave. #116,
San Jose, California 95117
408.985.0846 BarbGris@aol.com

September 15, 2014

To: CureQuick Insurance, Grievance Coordinator
P.O. Box 248
Summit, N.J. 97901

Re: Client Jack Klutz
CureQuick ID #: NPG5679020
Client DOB: 03/09/58
CPT Code: 90837
Dates of Service: 5/1/2014, 5/7/2014
                5/14/2014, 5/30/2014
Claim#: 98765432-00
Total Amount Charged: $400.00

NOTE: Give as much information as possible about the member and claim

To Whom It May Concern:

I am writing to take advantage of the provider dispute process in reference to the denial of payment for four psychotherapy sessions 5/1/14 through 5/30/14 with my client, Jack Klutz.

I initially submitted this claim online via OfficeAlly.com on 6/30/14. When I had not received payment by 7/30/14 I contacted CureQuick Claims Department (800-555-1234) and spoke to Marianne C. (call confirmation #C00691936264086). She said she saw no record of the claim and suggested I mail it to claims address 123 Lost Lane, Paper Trail, MN 55344. I sent it the next day. When I still had not received payment by 8/30/2014, I called CureQuick again at the same number (call confirmation #C00691936264333) and spoke to Steve C., a Claims Dept. supervisor. He said the claims address I had been given was incorrect for this member, and that the claim still had not been received. He said I should fax the claim and proof of online filing to him at 1-888-555-3333. The next day I printed out proof of filing from Office Ally and faxed this to him with a copy of the claim.

On 9/15/2014 I received the Explanation of Benefits, and all dates of service had been denied due to late filing (Claim #98765432-00, processed 9/07/14). I called CureQuick on 9/15/14 ((1-800-555-1234, call confirmation #C00691936264333) and spoke to claims representative Max G. He said I'd have to file an appeal to have the claim reconsidered.

I not only provided proof of timely filing (enclosed), but have made multiple attempts to file in a timely manner. I feel CureQuick should take responsibility for the fact that the claim was delayed in part due to misinformation given by CureQuick staff. In addition, I have provided medically necessary treatment for the member.

Please contact me if you need more information to reconsider this claim.
Sincerely,
I.M. Great, LMFT
Licensed Marriage and Family Therapist MFC27210
NPI XXXXXXXX Tax ID #XXXXXXXXX

Questions and Answers

If I'm an out-of-network provider, and I've been paid, is it really my role to assist clients in appeals? Shouldn't it be my client's job to hound their plan for payment?

Don't worry; you aren't being codependent if you help a client with an appeal. In fact, many professional associations have ethical standards that require their therapist members to advocate for treatment they believe will benefit clients. Assisting a client with an appeal may even be required by state law.

What if the insurance plan wants to see copies of my case notes for the appeal?

If your client signed your standard release form (or the one on the CMS-1500), he has already agreed to allow the release of "any medical information or other information necessary" to process the claims. However, it is a good idea to get the client's permission to file an appeal on his behalf. You should explain the appeal process to him, and you may want to have him sign a specific release if you need to submit case notes as part of an appeal. If your client is hesitant to have his insurance company see these notes, you may suggest he call the insurance company to discuss his concerns about the confidential handling of his health information. Of course, your client always retains the option of paying out of pocket for the disputed sessions instead of undergoing a case review.

I want to appeal, but I didn't take good notes while treating this client. Can I write or rewrite my notes before submitting them?

No. This may be insurance fraud. You could ask the plan if they will accept a treatment summary, but be sure you give the date that the summary was written.

Will insurance continue to authorize sessions for my client while I'm appealing a decision?

This depends on the plan, and on the reason you were denied. When it is a clear-cut coverage issue (ex. "we don't cover that service"), it is unlikely. However, managed care plans will typically allow you to see the client (and will continue to reimburse you) while you go through the appeal process when there is a dispute over medical necessity and sometimes if you are asking for an exception to plan rules. This is not always the case, so always call and ask. For a crisis case, seek an expedited review with the health plan, so that the outcome can be determined in a matter of days. If needed, contact your state Department of Insurance for advice (see state DOI contact information in Appendix A on Page 129). Be sure that the client is aware of any financial risks involved with continuing in therapy (for example, if the denial is upheld, the client may owe for sessions that took place in the interim). You may consider collecting for each session just in case the appeal is not successful, reimbursing if it is.

If the insurance company requests that I repay an overpayment, and I am contesting it, can I delay repayment while I appeal?

Usually, yes, but be sure to ask the insurance plan for its policy. In cases where repayment is requested, call the plan (or the financial recovery service, if you've been contacted by one), ask for an extension, and have your intended appeal documented by them, so you don't get any threatening letters when they don't receive payment. Also, you don't want them to begin trying to collect by withholding future payments on this or other cases. This happens when you don't repay CureQuick for one client, they decide to hold back payments they owe you for their other members until the "debt" is paid off. For this reason, try to get something in writing verifying that they have given you an extension, as sometimes I've experienced they have no record of this conversation.

My claim was denied because I didn't have an authorization in place on the date of service. Is there anything I can do?

Call the plan – you may need to talk to a case manager. Sometimes you can get them to retro-authorize (or back-date) a treatment authorization for that date of service (see Retro-Authorizations, Page 54). Then resubmit the claim with a note attached, including the new authorization number. Remember, you can't bill the client for a denial if it was due to your error.

14

Electronic Billing
With or Without a Computer
ℰℴ ℭℨ

Insurance, computers, and change -- three things many therapists avoid like the plague. Perhaps this is why as a group we have been slow to embrace electronic billing, despite the many benefits. A 2006 *Psychotherapy Finances* survey showed that only 23 percent of solo practitioners filed electronic claims.[42] In fact, only 55 percent of those surveyed used a computer to manage their practices in any way. While these numbers have surely increased significantly since this survey, it could be argued that the survey's conclusions still hold true: "What is clear is that mental health professionals continue to be the most technophobic businesspeople in America."

Despite this, the press for change is on. Insurance plans continually encourage providers to do all their transactions online instead of by phone. Paper claims may soon become obsolete, and insurance plans may only accept electronic claims. In fact, many insurance plans are requiring new providers to have internet access and to submit claims electronically.

While many of us use computers for little more than sending e-mails to Aunt Gladys or posting pictures of our children on Facebook, this magical plastic box gives us 24-hour access to most insurance plans. In addition to electronic billing, insurance company websites may enable you to:

- ▶ Check benefits and eligibility
- ▶ Check authorization status, number of sessions authorized, and expirations
- ▶ Download forms and applications, and submit requests for more sessions
- ▶ Submit claims and check claim status
- ▶ Update your practice information and availability to see new clients
- ▶ View lists of network providers (to assist with referrals)
- ▶ Create a personal statement and practice profile, which prospective clients can view
- ▶ Access provider articles, newsletters, and contract information
- ▶ Access medical necessity guidelines, appeal procedures, etc.
- ▶ Correspond with insurance company staff and ask questions

Types of Electronic Billing

Electronic billing is the submission of claims to the insurance plan via the Internet. But there is more than one way to do this. You don't even need a computer -- you only need to hire someone who does! Here are the four most common types of electronic billing:

1. **Submit directly at the plan's website.** When an insurance plan has the capacity to accept claims through their website, no special software is required on your end. You go to the plan website, log in with your provider ID and password (or follow the directions if you're a first time user), and follow the instructions to file claims. It's free and easy, even for the computer novice. It's usually fairly quick since the plan has the member's information already -- you don't have to enter it each time. You just add the session-specific information, such as dates of service and fees.

   Claims are filed directly and immediately with the insurance company, and you can print out immediate proof of filing. And the confidential information is encrypted so it is secure and HIPAA-compliant. Always print a copy of claims you submit online (or at least your claims submission confirmation page) to keep in the client's chart, and keep a record of when claims were filed.

   This is a good option for therapists who have don't have a large number of claims to file and/or who work with a limited number of insurance companies.

2. **Submit through a "claims clearinghouse" with a billing program.** This is a popular option for therapists who have (or are willing to get) simple billing or practice management software. The claims are transmitted from your computer's software program to a clearinghouse with whom you have contracted. A clearinghouse is a service that serves as an intermediary between you and the plans. The clearinghouse instantaneously converts the claims from your software to a HIPAA-compliant secure format, then transmits them electronically to each plan. So rather than sending a separate claim to each health insurer as a separate transaction, the clearinghouse serves as a central portal to transmit claims to multiple plans. You send your claims to the clearinghouse, and the clearinghouse then forwards the claims to the appropriate health insurer. Like giving your mail to the post office, they deliver it for you – but instantaneously!

   Sound expensive? There is at least one online clearinghouse, Office Ally (www.OfficeAlly.com), that will submit your claims without charge. They only charge a small fee if you want them to file claims by mail to health plans that are not on their extensive payer list. The clearinghouse catches many errors before the claim is sent, and e-mails you with the status of submitted claims, keeping a record of your submissions that you can use for proof of filing. And their customer service folks will walk even the most timid through the process. While there are other clearinghouses, Office Ally seems the most popular among therapists I've spoken to.

   Submitting via a clearinghouse may be an option to consider if you work with many insurance clients and/or multiple insurance companies, and if you have (or are willing to get) billing software. Contact the clearinghouse to make sure the plans you bill for are on the list of those payers they bill electronically, and that they can receive claims from your billing program. And before you purchase billing software, be sure it can interact with your chosen clearinghouse and insurance plans (for billing programs and Office Ally contact info, see Resources, Page 133).

3. **Submit through a claims clearinghouse <u>without</u> your own billing program.** Don't have your own billing software? Office Ally also has free online practice management software you can use called Practice Mate, which allows you to create and maintain a patient database, with client demographics, insurance information, and visit information, as well as to create Superbills and print or electronically submit claims (for contact information for Office Ally, see Resources, Page 133).

Again, this may be an option to consider if you work with many insurance clients and/or multiple insurance companies. It is a good idea to contact the clearinghouse to make sure the insurance plans you bill are on their payer list, and that they can receive claims from your particular billing program, if you have one.

4. **Submit through a billing service.** Here's an option for those of you who don't want to deal with computers or billing: Hire a billing service. A billing service is a good choice even if you have practice billing software but don't want to deal with claims submission and follow-up. After you fax, mail, or e-mail your client data to the billing service (you'll need to provide some log of clients seen, date seen, and procedure codes), the service will format and transmit the claims, and send them to the appropriate insurance company's website(s), or via mail, fax, or clearinghouse. For an additional fee, most billing services will follow-up on unpaid claims, deal with claims problems, verify insurance coverage for new clients, and track authorizations. Financial arrangements vary: Billing services may offer flat-fee pricing (a set amount per month regardless of number of claims filed), per-claim fees, or may charge a certain percentage of reimbursements received by insurance.

Karen Rose, MFT, loves her billing service. "They do all paperwork for my practice, including billing, tracking claims, dealing with unpaid claims, credentialing and re-credentialing. In fact, I now print on the back of my business cards, 'for billing questions, contact...' with their phone number. In this way, my clients contact them directly regarding billing and insurance issues, and I can just do therapy."[43] Sounds nice, huh?

What's In It for Therapists?

▶ **Faster payment.** The biggest payoff is that directly-filed electronic claims are instantaneously received by the insurance company, which greatly speeds payment. In addition, electronic claims are typically given priority processing status over paper claims. For example, in the past United Behavioral Health has reported that 90 percent of EAP claims and 50 percent of mental health or substance abuse claims submitted online go to a paid status <u>the next business day after they are received</u>, and 95 percent are paid within 14 business days.[44] This means better cash flow for you.

- **Less delay and denials due to errors.** Electronic billing has built-in alerts that prevent errors, and flags missing or invalid information before you file. If there is a problem with the claim, such as a missing or invalid CPT code or diagnosis code, it may be identified before the program allows you to submit the claim so you can correct it. You don't have to wait six weeks to find out when the claim is denied. Other errors, such as incorrect policyholder ID numbers or claims addresses, may be identified within a few days, so that you can submit a corrected claim. This quick identification of problems dramatically decreases the likelihood that your claim will be denied, which means faster payment and fewer hassles for you.

- **More security.** While therapists express concern about the confidentiality of client information submitted electronically, some insurance companies argue there is more security in electronic transmission than via "snail mail." Electronic claims are encrypted (translated into a coded message), so the file is secure and in compliance with HIPAA security standards.

- **Cost savings.** If you choose to file claims directly on the company's website or via a clearinghouse, you save the cost of claim forms, envelopes, and postage. And even a billing service may save money for you, once you figure in the cost of the time you would have spent doing all that they will do.

- **It's simple.** If you can fill out a CMS-1500 form by hand, you can do it online.

- **Reducing paper in your office, and saving trees.** Doing claims online, and signing up to allow the plan to e-mail you with newsletters or announcements, and direct deposit of your claims payment check can all save paper.

- **Easy tracking of claims.** You are typically given proof of filing, so that you can prove you filed in a timely manner if the insurance company ever questions this. You can always check the status of claims you've submitted, preventing "lost" claims.

Having said that, however, I add a warning: It is still important to follow up with your submissions if you are not paid in a timely fashion. I once contacted a plan when I hadn't been paid, and was told they hadn't received the claim from my clearinghouse. When I resubmitted the claim by fax it was denied for "lack of timely filing," and my appeal was denied, despite proof I provided of timely filing. While with most plans this proof would be all that would be needed to overturn this denial, in this case the plan said that they could not be held accountable for clearinghouse problems and that I was still responsible to be sure the plan received claims. While it is important to stay on top of unpaid claims, I won the appeal after filing a complaint with the State Department of Managed Care.

Questions and Answers

If I do electronic billing, do I have to deal with HIPAA regulations?

You bet. If you do any type of electronic billing using the internet, or if someone does it on your behalf (a billing service, a claims clearinghouse, an employee or independent contractor, etc.), or exchanges a client's information with insurance plans via e-mail, you automatically become a "covered entity" under HIPAA regulations. Once you are a covered entity, you will need to obtain a National Provider Identifier (NPI) to use on claims, and must give a Notice of Privacy Policies to all your clients. In addition, other HIPAA policies and procedures must be followed, both with your private pay and insurance clients. For more information on HIPAA, see the HIPAA section of this manual (Page 33), or the HIPAA/NPI Information section of Resources (Page 133).

Is buying a billing or practice management software a good idea for me?

This depends on the size of your insurance practice. Obviously, if you have only a few insurance clients, you might just fill out all claims by hand. However, the time may come soon when handwritten claims will be rejected. You may decide to go to the website of each client's insurance and submit claims there, if available, since these will be processed more quickly. However, if you have a large number of insurance clients, a billing program can be a real time saver. Even if you do file by mail, with one click many billing programs can take the client data you've entered into the program and print out the data into blank CMS-1500 forms for a whole month's worth of sessions. And, since computer-printed claim forms are typically processed more quickly by the plan, payment is faster. As was mentioned earlier, you may want to look into Office Ally, which has their own free practice management software and electronic filing program, so you don't need to buy your own (see Page 88 for more about Office Ally, or Resources, Page 133).

If you were thinking about buying your own practice management program for other reasons, the most basic programs start at about $50 - $120. If you are like me and your handwriting is so illegible you can't even read your own grocery list, a program that allows you to type session notes is worth looking into. These programs are more expensive (good ones average $500-$800). More deluxe programs may include session notes, authorization tracking, referral and cash flow statistics, medication trackers, sample treatment plans, reports, sample letters, practice expense logs, client scheduling, and the ability to export financial information to Quicken or QuickBooks. Remember that not all practice management programs offer the ability to bill electronically, and others charge extra for this feature.

Do all insurance plans accept electronic claims?

No, but most large ones do. For those that don't, you can bill by mail, have your clearinghouse bill by mail, or you can hire a billing service to bill those plans for you.

So, I can get paid electronically, too?

Yes, from many plans, and this is the wave of the future. The push is on for the "paperless office," and some plans, including Aetna, Blue Shield, and United Health Care, are now able to pay providers electronically through an Electronic Funds Transfer (EFT) right into your bank account. A representative from United Behavioral Health Care explained that once a provider signs up for UBH's Electronic Payment Service, claim payments are directly deposited. An e-mail notification is then sent to the therapist, and EOBs may be viewed and downloaded by going onto the UBH Website. This is available whether you submit claims electronically or by mail. While this service is currently voluntary, the UBH representative said he anticipated it would soon be company policy to handle all claims in this manner, but that exceptions would be made (such as for low-volume providers, those who share a tax ID number, or for clinicians who don't have Internet access or a bank account). Some providers – like me -- don't like electronic payment because even though you may get an e-mail alerting you to a payment, you typically must go online to view EOBs to see how much was paid for which clients and what dates of service.

Where can I get more information about billing software and electronic billing?

A list of some popular practice billing software can be obtained from many professional associations (see "Resources," Page 133). Consider carefully what you need your software to do. I spent a lot of money on mine since I wanted it to do a lot, including keeping track of client notes, medications, payments, and an electronic billing module. Others only need one that completes the CMS-1500 form for them. In the Resources section, I've given the names of some websites that list billing programs and give links to the websites of these programs. I have also listed some other resources for electronic billing, and the names of organizations with mental health billing specialties. It can also be helpful to call the insurance companies you work with (or want to work with) and ask for their electronic billing help desk. They may be able to give you the names of practice software programs and clearinghouses with which their system is compatible.

Any recommendations when it comes to choosing a billing service?

I wish I had a resource list of billing services to give you, a list, but I don't. Get referrals from other mental health professionals in your area. I recommend you find a service that specializes in mental health billing, which can be quite different than medical billing – you need someone who stays on top of the ever-changing world of mental health insurance coding and billing. You also should find someone who extensive experience working with other therapists in your state. They should have lots of experience working with plans in your state -- insurance plans operate so differently in each state, and that experience with the different plan expectations can make all the difference. Consider carefully what exactly you want a billing service to do for you, and shop around, getting estimates from different services. Write out and sign clear agreements about all expectations and fees. Interview billers and call their references. Remember that you don't necessarily need to find someone who has an office close to you – depending on what you want the billing service to do; it is possible that all communication service may take place via phone, fax, or e-mail. Most importantly, monitor them closely – ask for regular reports on which plans have been billed for what clients and what dates of services, so if something happens with the billing service you could pick up where they left off.

15

Clinical Issues & Confidentiality

ଯ ଓଃ

So as Jack's therapy progresses, how will taking his insurance affect his treatment?

Clinical Issues

▶ **You may need to spend some session time discussing coverage.** You may need to educate Jack about issues such as network vs. out-of network provider options, copayments, deductibles, limitations of coverage, and pre-authorization. Jack may think he has coverage for unlimited yearly visits, but may not know that these sessions will be given to him only if his plan determines that they are medically necessary.

▶ **Brief, goal emphasis.** Perhaps the most significant way that managed care has changed therapy is the emphasis on short-term, cognitive-behavioral, evidence-based, and symptom-focused therapies. And because insurance is illness-based, managed care plans aim for symptom reduction instead of the in-depth exploration of personal growth and development, life goals, career counseling, communication skills, character flaws, or childhood trauma. And it isn't just that the insurance plans are coming to expect counseling to be briefer and more goal-directed – this has affected the expectations of many clients.

▶ **Clients may stop coming when benefits end.** Instead of continuing and paying out of pocket when he runs out of sessions, Jack may be tempted to take a break and restart counseling when his benefits renew. It can be a challenge to help clients make treatment decisions that are not based solely on benefits.

▶ **Clients may be unable to see the therapist of their choice if the therapist is not covered by insurance.** If Jack changes to a health plan where you are not a participating provider, or if you leave the CureQuick provider panel, he may not be able to afford to continue with you, and might need to find a new therapist. In many cases, this can also mean that Jack is unable to see the professional best suited to meet his needs, or a specialist you would like him to see (i.e. a psychiatrist with an expertise in treating pail phobias), if the specialist is not a network provider.

▶ **Think outside the box.** While once-a-week therapy is often the norm, if Jack only has limited sessions (left on an authorization, or available each year), he may not want to space sessions out.

- **You may need to set goals that take into account the client's insurance plan and its limitations.** If the client has only a few sessions, and does not have the ability to continue with you after these benefits run out, it is important to set realistic goals that can be achieved in the given time frame. You may choose to become more focused in your work, and limit the scope of treatment to one specific issue.

- **Monitor your negative counter-transference.** It is easy to get resentful about the plan's fee discounts, limitations, and paperwork, and take it out on your insurance clients. You may find yourself giving preferential treatment to full-fee, private pay clients, like calling them back first, or giving them the best time slots. Or you may feel annoyed when your (discount fee) managed care client Jack discusses his recent luxury car purchase or yachting adventures.

- **High-risk and substance abuse cases may mean more contact with case managers.** It is wise to share any serious concerns about risk issues (suicide attempts, suicide risk, violence, substance abuse, homicide, child abuse) with case managers at the plan. This helps protect you in the event that Jack destabilizes, harms himself, or harms someone else. Case managers can also be helpful in suggesting resources the plan may provide or cover. For example, if you found Jack had become dependent on alcohol, you might contact CureQuick to discuss treatment options covered by the plan before presenting them to Jack.

- **If you'd like to see Jack more than one hour daily or weekly, you may need permission from the plan.** Some plans will only reimburse for one hour of outpatient therapy per day, and one session per week, unless prior approval is given. As always, ask the insurance company.

- **If Jack can't afford his copayment, co-insurance or deductible**, you may be tempted to help him out by waiving it. Read more about why you shouldn't, and other ways to help Jack out, on Page 101.

Confidentiality Issues

When discussing the topic of insurance, perhaps one of the biggest concerns of therapists and clients is confidentiality. Despite state laws and HIPAA protections, clients who use their insurance are concerned about how their private health information will be used, and with whom it may be shared. This is especially understandable since the sensitive topics

discussed in therapy (such as a client's sexual orientation, HIV status, infidelity, or abuse of drugs or alcohol) could have devastating consequences if disclosed to the wrong parties. A 2005 survey conducted by the California Healthcare Foundation found that 67 percent of respondents were concerned about the privacy of their medical records, and 52 percent were concerned that insurance claims information might be used by an employer to limit job opportunities.[45] In fact, 13 percent of those surveyed said they had done something to protect the privacy of their medical history, presenting a potential risk to their health. These protective behaviors included paying out of pocket to avoid submitting an insurance claim, not seeking care to avoid disclosure, avoiding a visit to the doctor for treatment of certain conditions, asking a provider not to write down a health condition, giving inaccurate or incomplete information on a medical form, requesting care under an assumed name, or asking a therapist not to take notes. The survey also found that these clients were largely unaware of their privacy rights.

Yet despite these concerns, patients reported a favorable view of new health technology which allows treating providers to store and share medical records, with a majority (59%) willing to share personal health information when it could result in better medical treatment.

What do I say when Jack asks, "how much of what I say in here can get back to my employer?"

One response would be to say something like, "What you say in our session, and even your very presence here, is confidential. It is my ethical and legal duty, and one which I take very seriously. This means that even if your wife or boss called and asked if you were here, I couldn't confirm or deny it, unless I had your written consent. Your insurance company is also obliged by law to protect your confidentiality. No information about the issues you are discussing is released by me or by your plan to your employer, unless you are a mandatory management referral. The health plan may report some statistical information to the employer (for example, how many visits were used overall by employees), but data is not client-specific, so your name or identifying information should not be connected with this data." You could then review exceptions to confidentiality, which should also be in your treatment agreement (see sample treatment agreement, Page 143).

If Jack is still concerned about confidentiality issues, you might outline the security measures you take to protect his private information, physical files, practice software, and files related to computer or electronic billing. You might also recommend that he contact his insurance company to discuss the plan's policies for the handling of his confidential client information. Of course, he may always choose to pay out of pocket instead.

Should Jack be concerned that using his insurance might be troublesome for him later if he applies for future health or life insurance policies?

Clients are often concerned if they use insurance that this could in some way come back to haunt them. They might be particularly concerned that it might affect their ability to get a future health or life insurance policy. But things have changed a bit in this arena.

In the past, if Jack used his insurance he would be given a diagnosis, and as his therapist you would fill out paperwork about his treatment (minimally a claim form). Jack might be concerned that such a "paper trail" of his treatment and mental health condition could become a problem for him somehow later on. This most frequently became a problem if Jack lost his employer-sponsored group health coverage and needed to apply for an individual health plan. Unlike group plans, where applicants are not asked medical history questions, individual health or life insurance plan applicants go through medical scrutiny.

In the past, if Jack was honest about his pre-existing health conditions (including mental health conditions), the plan might have denied Jack coverage altogether, or excluded coverage for the "pre-existing health condition" for which you treated him, or charged a premium significantly higher than normal since he is considered at higher risk for illness.

But the good news is that the Affordable Care Act now prohibits these discriminatory health care plan practices, both for children and adults. Health plans covered by the ACA must charge the same for members with pre-existing health conditions as for healthy members (for more on the ACA, see Page 36).

Unfortunately, the ACA does not apply to life insurance plans, so life insurance plans are still able to discriminate based on pre-existing health conditions. A diagnosis and "paper trail" could also become an issue if Jack is pursuing Top Secret clearance or applying for other special government clearances.

If Jack still isn't sure whether to use his insurance, here is something to keep in mind: On the individual life insurance plan application or top secret clearance application, Jack may be asked if he has attended therapy within a certain period of time prior to the application, with whom, and some treatment details. If he answers these questions truthfully, he may be asked to sign a release so that Jack's therapist can be contacted about the presenting issues, diagnosis, course and length of treatment. <u>So the outcome may be the same whether Jack uses his insurance to pay for your sessions or pays out of pocket</u>.

Should I make Jack aware of the type of information I have to send to his insurance? Should I tell him that the plan has the right to look at his case notes?

"I can't stress enough that whenever you bill an insurance company for something, they have the right to see your notes -- even if you're not contracted," says Susan Frager, a former case manager and mental health billing specialist.[46] Any third party you or your client bills has the right to determine the medical necessity of treatment. You may want to inform all your insurance clients about the types of information sent to an insurance plan. You could write a few lines in your treatment agreement specifically identifying the kind of information you may be asked to release (see sample agreement, Page 143). Or you could do it on a case-by-case basis, only informing clients who express confidentiality concerns. You could show Jack blank copies of any treatment update or claim forms you may need to submit to his plan, and explain the type of information required to process claims or request authorizations. You might also explain that if he chooses to use insurance, he is agreeing to allow the health plan to view your case notes, if needed, to approve further treatment or ensure the quality of your care. Then Jack can make an informed choice whether to use his insurance. While you could stress that insurance plans are also obligated to protect his confidentiality, he might want to contact his plan to find out more about how it handles confidential data. If he doesn't feel comfortable after this exchange, he can choose to pay out of pocket.

What if it becomes clear that I will need to disclose sensitive information in Jack's case in order to get more sessions approved?

While the client may have signed a release allowing you to disclose "any information necessary" to obtain insurance reimbursement, a therapist should make every effort to protect a client's confidential private health information. Don't reveal any more information than you must in order to get treatment authorized or a claim processed -- using or disclosing more than the minimum necessary protected health information can be a HIPAA violation (see Page 35). But sometimes it will be necessary to reveal sensitive information in order to receive reimbursement or get authorization for continued treatment. It may be wise to talk with Jack in these cases about the information that will need to be revealed so he can make an informed choice about whether to allow the release. Again, he may decide he would rather not use his insurance to pay for your sessions if this type of exchange of information is necessary. Be sure to document your conversation and your client's decision, and have him sign a Private-Pay Agreement if he decides to waive his right to use his insurance (see Sample Private-Pay Agreement, Page 149).

Is the insurance company bound by confidentiality laws?

While laws vary in each state, insurance companies can be sued and fined heavily if they negligently release a client's private health information in most situations (for example, to an employer, or any third party) without a signed release from the client, unless permitted by law.

I have a client who is seeking therapy, using her husband's insurance plan, but she doesn't want her husband to know she is in treatment. Can he find out?

Whenever a plan member (in this case, the wife) uses benefits, the primary subscriber (here, the husband) normally receives a copy of treatment authorizations and claims payments. These might even be addressed to him, and would arrive by mail (or e-mail) at the address the plan has on record. While these may have only basic information on them, it would alert your client's husband that she is receiving treatment, from whom, the treating provider's address, and possibly even what type of treatment is being received. Even if your client is the policyholder, she will get this documentation, so there is a risk that he might open this mail. This is a fact most clients are not aware of, which could be a significant factor in their decision to use their insurance, especially in certain cases. I advise telling clients up front if you suspect this might be an issue of concern, especially in domestic violence or similar cases. Your client might want to call her insurance plan -- in certain circumstances the plan might be able to arrange for correspondence to come to her at another address, or help her in some other way.

Are there any special precautions I have to take for insurance records?

Most insurance companies require client records to be kept in a secure manner (for example, locked or password-protected). You should have policies and procedures for protecting the confidentiality of any stored or electronically-transmitted client information, or for purging of records in a manner that protects confidentiality. If you are a HIPAA covered entity (see Chapter 7 for more on this), and even if you aren't, you will want to follow the guidelines outlined in HIPAA for the security of all client records.

16

13 Ways to Jeopardize Your License
Common Types of Insurance Fraud

✻ ❦ ✺

Most of us become therapists because we want to help people, not because we are financial wizards. In all our years of coursework, we may never have taken a class in running a small business, or in dealing with insurance plans. Because we may not be well-informed about the financial aspects of our practices, we can end up making decisions that we don't even know are illegal or unethical.

In some cases, our resentment about contract restrictions and discounts may cause us to be less than completely honest in our billing. After all, you may feel, these big insurance plans can afford it, and no one will find out. In other cases, you may bend the truth in a well-intentioned attempt to assist clients, to help them afford therapy. "Some of these practices have become so commonplace that many healthcare practitioners forget that what they are really doing is misrepresenting their services to insurance companies solely for the purpose of getting reimbursed," writes Mary Riemersma, former Executive Director of the California Association of Marriage and Family Therapists.[47]

So how exactly do we know we've left the land of trying to help clients, and entered the territory of insurance fraud? Michael Brandt, a fraud investigator for HealthNet Insurance, writes that "health care fraud is deception or misrepresentation by providers, employers, members, or any person acting on their behalf with knowledge that the deception could result in some unauthorized payment or benefit."[48] Note that this definition includes people "acting on your behalf," such as billing services or clearinghouses you have hired.

Here's a quick rundown of some common fraud traps that are easy to fall into:

1. **Choosing or changing a diagnosis to expedite or guarantee payment.** I am often asked, "what diagnosis should I put on the claim so I'll be paid?" My answer is, of course, "put down whatever is true, without regard for reimbursement." Otherwise, this fits the core part of fraud's definition: misrepresentation. But frequently therapists will fall into the trap of:

    ▶ **Giving a diagnosis when none exists.** It is fraud to submit a claim giving a diagnosis of a mental illness when one does not exist. This may be especially tempting if a client or couple seeks counseling for issues related to self-esteem, communication, career issues, or personal growth, but there is no diagnosable mental illness present (as classified in the DSM or ICD). If you do choose a diagnosis, be confident you could defend it later to an insurance company representative, or in court, if it came to that. Document the symptoms that support your diagnosis in your case notes. Remember that a V-code alone typically will not be covered, except by EAPs.

    ▶ **Changing Diagnosis:** It is sometimes tempting to give the client a more serious diagnosis than they actually have in the hopes that this will give them better or longer coverage. For example, you may feel if you give Jack a diagnosis of Major Depression instead of Adjustment Disorder on the treatment update, Jack might be given a larger number of authorized sessions. Jack may even ask you to do this. But this is fraud. In other cases, such as when the client has a "pre-existing condition" clause, insurance may exclude coverage for a particular condition that was present before their coverage began. Changing the diagnosis to "get around" this clause is also fraud. While you may always add a diagnosis, a diagnosis should not be changed unless a mistake was made in the original diagnosis, additional information has led you to another diagnosis, or the client's condition has changed.

    ▶ **Under-diagnosing:** For example, Jack may ask you not to tell the plan about his alcohol abuse. But it could be considered fraud if you only put down a diagnosis of Adjustment Disorder and not substance abuse. Why? Because the insurance plan might have made different authorization or reimbursement decisions if they knew the correct diagnosis. Also, problems could arise if there are discrepancies between your treatment notes and your billing diagnosis. While I have heard therapists say they give the same "innocuous" diagnosis to all their insurance clients, this is clearly fraud, and you find yourself in trouble if this pattern was ever noticed, or if your records were audited.

    To reiterate, never give a diagnosis that you couldn't defend in court, or that would make you lose sleep the night before you had to testify. Log the symptoms of the diagnosis in the client's chart.

2. **Billing insurance for cancelled or missed sessions without making it clear that the appointment was missed.** While it is permissible to bill for a missed appointment, you must make it clear on the claim that the client did not attend the session – don't use a CPT code that would give the impression that the session took place. I do not know of any insurance companies that pay for cancelled sessions or no-shows, though some EAPs do; check your contract (if you are a plan provider) or call the insurance plan. If you are allowed to bill for missed sessions, ask the

insurance plan what CPT code to use on the bill or claim. Be sure "missed" or "cancelled" is clearly indicated. Remember that some insurance contracts do not allow you to bill the client for missed sessions; others allow it when the client has agreed in writing and in advance to pay for missed sessions.

3. **Charging the health plan more than your usual fee if you are an out-of-network provider.** In your practice, you should have a designated "full fee" that you charge for sessions. This doesn't mean you need to abandon your sliding-fee scale. It is OK to slide <u>down</u> from your usual fee, just not <u>up</u> past your full fee when billing insurance plans. While this is not an issue for network therapists, who have a contracted fee, if you are an out-of-network therapist, it may be tempting to charge insurance companies more per session than your full fee. It would be fraud, for example, to charge Jack's insurance $175 if your full fee is $125 – it is a misrepresentation of your actual fee.

4. **Waiving client copayments, co-insurance, or deductible in advance.** You may not bill the insurance and tell the client he doesn't need to pay his copayment or deductible. As part of your contract, you agreed to collect copayments, and Jack agreed in his contract with the plan to pay his copayments, so waiving these is a violation of those contracts. More importantly, if your contracted rate with CureQuick is $70, and you told Jack before the session he didn't need to pay his 30% coinsurance ($21), you are billing the insurance for $70 with the intention of only collecting $49 for the session, which is fraud.

Does this mean you can't offer a sliding-scale fee? Not when there is a flat copayment, as that is a set amount. But if Jack has a coinsurance (where he pays a percentage of the contracted rate), you might choose to slide your fee. For example, if you cut your fee to $50, Jack's coinsurance would only be $15. But in this case you should bill the insurance plan only $50 per session, so that you are being honest about the amount you intend to collect for the session. Another option: Avoid using insurance altogether and simply take a reduced rate per visit in cash, or see him pro-bono.

Keep in mind that waiving copayments or coinsurances in advance is not the same as forgiving balances the client has left unpaid. The latter is acceptable as long as you have made reasonable attempts to collect and as long as the debt wasn't waived at the beginning of treatment.

5. **<u>Not</u> balance-billing the client if you are an out-of-network provider.** As was said, network providers are not permitted to bill the client for any amount above their contracted rate. If you are an out-of-network provider and you have not been paid in full by the client, and you are billing on the client's behalf, you <u>must</u> collect the difference between the session fee stated on the claim form and what the plan paid. Otherwise, if you billed the plan for a $100 session, and did not collect any part of this amount, the $100 you put on the claim was a fraudulent amount. Once again, you have the option of sliding your fee before filing a claim, but you must report this reduced fee on the claim form.

6. **Billing for writing reports or treatment summaries, or for consultations with other providers, using a therapy CPT code.** Most insurance companies will not reimburse for administrative time, training, or consultations, and many won't allow you to bill your client for them. Check your contract (if you are a network

provider). If you are allowed to bill insurance for these services, use appropriate CPT codes, not those you use for therapy sessions. If your contract with the health plan allows you to bill your client, be sure your client agrees in writing and in advance.

7. **Reporting that you provided individual therapy when you saw a couple, or vice versa in order to be paid for the session.** Let's say you are working with Jack and Jill as a couple, but you want to see Jill alone for one session. On the claim for that session, you might think you should continue to list Jack as the identified client and use the couples therapy CPT code 90847, thinking of Jill's session as part of couples therapy. However, it is possible if the plan had known it was Jill alone they might have made a different reimbursement decision, so it is important to give them as much information as possible so as not to appear fraudulent. It may be more appropriate to use CPT code 90846 (family therapy without patient present). Or you can make her the identified client for this session, but you'd need to make sure she has coverage and a diagnosis -- she might also need her own treatment authorization. Conversely, if you are afraid the plan won't cover your ongoing couples sessions with Jack and Jill, you cannot use a CPT code that gives the impression that you met alone with Jack.

8. **Providing a couples therapy session, and billing both partners' insurance companies for an individual therapy session.** Because the CPT codes are different, this is misrepresenting the service provided. It is also duplicate billing for a single service. You may bill both insurance plans for couples therapy, but you need to bill the primary insurance first, and secondary insurance after the primary has paid, letting each insurance plan know about the other's coverage and payments. You must also inform each company that the other partner has coverage (for more on double coverage, see Chapter 17).

9. **Having someone else sign your claims, or having interns or unlicensed associates sign in a way that might make them appear licensed.** If you are not licensed, or your license is not covered under the health plan, you may <u>not</u> have a covered license holder sign for you. The consequences for misrepresenting the service provider can be severe, including jail time, community service, repaying the insurance company, money damages, and potential loss of license. Interns and associates are typically not covered by insurance, and so should not bill for care without plan approval. If the insurance company does reimburse interns or associates, the treating therapist and supervisor should both sign, identifying themselves on the claim with titles such as "treating therapist" and "supervising

therapist." Some states require that interns spell out their status (ex. spelling out "MFT Intern" instead of "MFTI").

10. **Billing two insurance companies for the same service(s) with the intent to collect your full fee from both of them.** The bottom line? You may not collect more than your full fee for any given session.

11. **Billing for services you didn't provide.** This includes billing for missed sessions or phone sessions as if the client attended. <u>Another version of this would be billing for a 45 minute session even though Jack was 30 minutes late, and you only saw him for 15 minutes</u>.

12. **Rewriting case notes before an insurance case review, audit or appeal.** This is equivalent to falsifying documents, and you may be guilty of insurance fraud.

13. **Changing service dates.** You may be tempted to change session dates on the claim in order to be covered by an authorization that has since expired, or back-date sessions because a client has since lost coverage. Or if you know the insurance plan won't cover your two-hour session, you might think about submitting a bill for two separate one-hour sessions on different days. However, reporting that you saw a client on a day you didn't is insurance fraud (see more on two-hour sessions on Page 70).

"Do not allow yourself to be misled or manipulated by your clients who convincingly ask for your assistance in reducing their financial burdens at the expense of their insurance companies," writes Mary Riemersma, former Executive Director of the California Association of Marriage and Family Therapists. "You are the therapist, the one in control of the situation, and you should be the role model. The costs to you as the therapist can be very great should you be charged with insurance fraud or some other violation of law."[49] In addition, from a clinical perspective, you would be essentially entering into an illicit conspiracy with your client against the insurance company, an agreement which could taint the therapy, and negatively affect the therapist/client relationship.

17

Couples, Families, & "Double Coverage"

❧ ☙

When Jack fell down the hill, his wife Jill came tumbling after him – literally and emotionally. Things have been pretty tense at their household, and Jack requests couples therapy instead of individual sessions.

While discussed at different points in this manual, many of the following points bear repeating here, since treating couples brings up challenges when working with insurance.

Couples or Family Therapy

▶ **Will insurance cover it?** Most insurance plans and employee assistance programs cover couples and family therapy, but a few plans don't. If covered, plans typically will cover couples or family therapy only when the client listed on the claim has a diagnosable mental disorder. Be ready to explain to the plan why you feel couples or family counseling is the best modality for treating the disorder (it is not enough to say "because the client wanted it"). But remember: it is insurance fraud to overstate or create a diagnosis for a family member for the purpose of ensuring reimbursement (for more about fraud, see Chapter 16).

▶ **Be sure to use the CPT code for couples or family therapy (90847).**

▶ **Instead of asking if a plan covers couples therapy,** ask when you call, "do you cover CPT code 90847 for this member to treat his diagnosis?" This makes it clear that there is a diagnosed client, and that it is not just a session aimed at personal growth or couples communication. You may be able to argue that you believe that couples therapy will most effectively bring about the reduction of Jack's symptoms. You may also want to ask if the plan covers CPT code 90846 (family psychotherapy without patient present), in case you feel this might be helpful in the future.

▶ **While you may not like thinking in terms of "identified client," for billing purposes, you need to choose one.** The member of the couple with the diagnosis is the identified client on the claim. If both have diagnoses, either may be the identified client, unless one is clearly the focus of treatment. If both have diagnoses, you may want to choose the one who has primary insurance (see "Double Coverage," Page 106).

▶ **If providing couples therapy, and you want to see one member of the couple alone,** clearly identify who attended the session on the billing form. Let's say you are working with Jack and Jill as a couple, and Jack is your identified client, but for one session you want to see Jill alone. It may be most appropriate to use the CPT code 90846 (family therapy without patient present), but it is a good idea to ask the plan first if they cover this code. Otherwise, to bill insurance for Jill's session, she must have coverage, a diagnosis, be identified as the client on the claim for this session, and she might need her own treatment authorization for this session. If she is not covered by any insurance plan, she might pay out of pocket for this session.

Do not bill Jack's insurance in a way that gives the impression that Jack was present in your individual session with Jill (i.e., listing Jack as the client on the claim).

▶ **If both partners have an EAP session benefit, and you are seeing them as a couple,** you might be able to bill some sessions under Jack's EAP authorization, and then have Jill get her own authorization, so that you could bill the next set under her name. In this way, if each family member has eight EAP sessions, you could do 16 EAP couples sessions. However, it is wise to check with the employee assistance program to be sure this is allowed. Remember that the intention of the EAP program is for assessment, very brief treatment, and referral. If in the assessment it becomes clear that your client will need longer-term treatment, the EAP program may want you to immediately refer the client to his/her health plan for treatment.

▶ **Can I see two clients from the same family for ongoing individual sessions?** Some managed care companies frown on allowing one therapist to see two clients from the same family separately for ongoing individual therapy. Some will not authorize it, while many do not have a specific policy against it. If you would like to see two members of the same family individually, and you have a good clinical reason for doing so, contact the insurance company to be sure they allow it.

Double Coverage: When a Client or Couple is Covered by Two Plans

You are seeing Jack and Jill for couples therapy, and both have insurance coverage. How do you deal with this?

When a client or couple is covered by two plans, things get complicated. This may happen when both have coverage, or when the client with the diagnosis is covered by two plans. Remember: The client must have a diagnosis – a V-code alone is not usually enough.

While the process varies somewhat depending on circumstances, in most cases, you would:

1. Determine whose insurance is the "primary insurance" (not sure whose insurance is primary? See "Questions and Answers" Page 109).
2. Collect deductibles and/or copayments as if the primary plan is the only coverage.
3. Submit a claim to the primary plan. If Jack has the diagnosis, and his plan is the primary insurance, identify Jack as the client on the claim, and use the CPT code for a couples session (90847). If using the CMS-1500 claim form, fill in the details about Jill's plan when asked about "other insurance" (boxes 9, 9a, 9d, and 11d).
4. Jack's plan will send an Explanation of Benefits (EOB) with a payment or denial.
5. Then you (or the couple, in some cases) may submit a claim to the secondary insurance plan (which in our example would be Jill's) to collect whatever portion the primary plan did not pay. Be sure to include a copy of the primary plan's EOB. Jill's plan will typically reimburse the couple for their out-of-pocket expenses for the session – their deductibles and copayments.

6. Remember: The total recoverable rate for the session may not exceed your full fee (if you are an out-of-network provider) or your contracted rate (if you are in-network with either plan). Overpayments must be refunded to the secondary plan, or this would be fraud. If you are paid in full you will also have to reimburse the clients if they paid you copayments. If you are out-of-network with both plans, your clients are responsible for any part of your full fee that was not paid by both plans (see the examples that follow).

Huh?? Let's try some examples.

Jack and Jill are in couples therapy. Only Jack has a diagnosis, but both have health plans (Jack's is CureQuick, Jill's is BeWell). You determine that Jack's plan is primary (see Page 109). Your full fee is $100. Jack's plan pays network providers $67, and Jill's plan pays network providers $70. Both plans pay 70% of this contracted rate for network providers. For out-of-network providers they pay 50% of the UCR (the maximum allowable rate). You find out from submitting claims that both have a UCR of $90. Neither has a deductible. *

	Example 1 You are a Network Provider for Both Plans	**Example 2** You're Out-of-Network for Both Plans	**Example 3** You're In-Network only for the Primary Plan	**Example 4** You're In-Network only for the Secondary Plan
Primary Insurance Pays: (70% in-network, 50% out-of-network)	**$46.90** (70% of $67, your contracted rate with the primary plan)	**$45** (50% of the plan's UCR, in this case $90)	**$46.90** (70% of $67, your contracted rate with the primary plan)	**$45** (50% of the plan's UCR, in this case $90)
Secondary Insurance Pays:** (70% in-network, 50% out-of-network)	**$20.10**** (The difference between your rate of $67 with the primary plan and the $46.90 the primary paid)	**$45**** (subtract what the primary plan paid from the primary plan's UCR of $90)	**$20.10**** (The difference between your rate of $67 with the primary and the $46.90 the primary paid)	**$25**** (subtract what the primary plan paid from your $70 contracted rate with the secondary plan)
Client Will Pay:	**$0**	**$10**	**$0**	**$0**
Total You Can Collect	**$67** (your contract rate with primary plan)	**$100** (your full fee)	**$67** (your contract rate with primary plan)	**$70** (your contract rate with secondary)
Must I be the one to bill the primary plan?	**Yes** (It is in your contract with both plans to do so)	**No** (You or the couple can, since you didn't sign a contract agreeing to do it)	**Yes** (It is in your contract with this plan to do so)	**No** (You or the couple can, since you didn't sign a contract with this plan to do it)
Must I be the one to bill the secondary plan?	**Yes** (It is in your contract with both plans to do so)	**No** (The couple can -- you didn't sign a contract with any plan to do it)	**No** (The couple can -- you didn't sign a contract with the secondary to do it)	**Yes** (It is in your contract with the secondary plan to do it)

* Note: This information would change when either plan has a deductible – see Page 110.
** The secondary plan may mistakenly pay more – you must refund them if they do.

In Example 1, you are a network provider for both plans. Since in our example Jack's is primary, you collect his co-insurance, and then submit a claim to his plan, CureQuick. CureQuick sees your contracted rate is $67, and pays 70 percent of this amount, for a total of $46.90, leaving Jack a co-insurance of $20.10. You may then submit a claim to Jill's insurance, BeWell (you must do the billing, since you agreed to do this in your contract with Jill's plan). Attach a copy of CureQuick's EOB. BeWell pays the difference between your contract rate with the primary plan ($67) and the amount that was paid ($46.90), for a total of $20.10. You are limited to collecting a combined total of $67 (your contracted rate with the primary plan). If the secondary plan pays more than $20.10, you must refund it. You can't bill Jack for any difference between your full fee and your contract rate with the primary plan. And you must refund Jack for any payments he made to you.

In Example 2, you are not a provider for either network. Jack's plan is still primary. Because you are out-of-network, the client will likely pay you up front. Then when the claim is submitted CureQuick will reimburse $45, which is 50 percent of $90. Why didn't they pay 50 percent of your full fee $100? In this case, $90 is the UCR, which the amount the plan has determined is the maximum payable to out-of-network providers. The couple may then bill Jill's plan, BeWell, attaching a copy of CureQuick's EOB. BeWell should pay the difference between CureQuick's UCR of $90 and the $45 that was already paid, for a total of $45. The good news? As an out-of-network provider, you are not bound by any UCR from either plan, and collect your full fee for the session from the clients even if his insurance plan sets UCRs. It is helpful to tell clients up front (or have a treatment agreement that states) that they owe whatever insurance doesn't pay (see Sample Treatment Agreement, 143).

In Example 3, you are only contracted with the primary plan, CureQuick (Jack's plan). However, you will notice the payments are the same as Example 1. Why? Because the session is processed according to the terms of the primary plan. You collect co-insurance from Jack, then bill CureQuick. CureQuick will pay $46.90, which is 70 percent of your $67 contract rate, leaving Jack a co-insurance of $20.10. The couple may then bill Jill's plan, BeWell, attaching a copy of CureQuick's EOB. BeWell calculates the difference between your contract rate with the primary plan and the amount the primary paid ($46.90), reimbursing the client for the co-insurance they paid of $20.10. You can't collect more than $67 for this session (your contracted rate with the primary plan). You may not bill the client for any difference between your full fee and your contract rate with the primary plan.

In Example 4, you are only contracted with Jill's plan, BeWell. Since Jack's plan is the primary, you still need to submit to his plan first. Because you are an out-of-network provider, CureQuick should pay $45, which is 50 percent of $90, leaving Jack a co-insurance of $45. Why didn't they pay 50 percent of your full fee $100? In our example, $90 is the UCR, which the amount the plan has determined is the maximum payable to out-of-network providers. You may then submit a claim to Jill's insurance, BeWell, attaching a copy of CureQuick's EOB (you must do the billing, since you agreed to do this in your contract with Jill's plan). BeWell will see that your contract rate with BeWell is $70, and will subtract what the primary plan paid ($45) from $70, and pay the remaining $25. If the secondary plan pays more than $25, you must refund it. You may not bill the client for any difference between your full fee and your contract rate with the secondary plan.

Are you thoroughly confused yet?

Questions and Answers

I've looked at your chart and examples, and this is NOT what the insurance plan representatives (or my billing expert) told me about double coverage, or how I've been paid.

I understand — when researching this book, I got all kinds of contradicting information (and downright misinformation) from even high-level folks at different plans. But customer service representatives, clinical case managers, and even network managers are typically not trained about these complicated double claims issues. Even most claims examiners don't know how this all works. However, after consulting with enough experts, I believe the information in this chapter is correct. The bottom line? You are accountable for knowing the terms of any contract you signed with the insurance plan(s), especially your contracted fee, and this is the maximum you can collect for any session if you are in-network with either plan -- no matter what the plan representatives may tell you.

What do I do if the secondary plan pays me too much, or more than my contracted rate? Can I keep the overpayment?

I wish I could say yes, but the answer is no. "You need to reimburse the secondary plan even though it is their mistake. The error is theirs for not looking at the primary [plan's] EOB and noting that there is a contract discount. It's a frequent error," says Susan Frager, a mental health billing expert.[50] "This gets sticky and really requires a claims examiner who knows what he or she is doing...and understands the difference between UCR and contracted rate. Often you get people that don't have a clue, unfortunately," says Frager. Remember, too, that accepting overpayments is fraud, and violates your contract with the plan.

Your examples make it sound like the plans will tell you their UCR up front.

Sometimes they will, sometimes they won't. Why wouldn't they? "They don't want to risk that the provider will inflate their charge. If you call, you may be told only that your billed charge is within their UCR, or is above it. So you end up having to wait for the first claim to come back to know what the UCR is," says Frager. However, it is worth asking on the first call. And this is one reason I recommend you bill soon after a client's first session.

Let's say Jack is covered by two plans (for example, because he works two jobs, or has his own plan and is a dependent on Jill's plan). Which is the primary insurance?

If only Jack has a diagnosis, he is the identified client. If Jack is covered by two insurance plans, and is the primary subscriber on his (CureQuick) plan and the dependent on another (say his wife's plan, BeWell), the plan where he is the primary subscriber or policyholder is considered the primary insurance.

If Jack is the primary policyholder on more than one plan, you may need to check the effective dates. In most cases, the plan that has covered Jack the longest would be designated as his primary insurance. If both plans have the same effective date, the primary plan may be the one with the earliest date of hire (that is, where he has worked longest). But this varies by insurance plan, so call and ask.

What if both partners have diagnoses and their own plans? Whose is primary?

If one is covered as the subscriber or policyholder on his/her plan, and the other is covered as a dependent (e.g., if Jill is covered by her parents' plan), the policyholder's plan will be the primary one. If both are policyholders on their own policies, and both have diagnoses, the "birthday rule" often applies. This means (according to two plan representatives I spoke to) that the primary insurance may be that of the client whose birthday falls earliest in the year (not necessarily the older person). No, I'm not kidding. But in some plans, the primary is the one that has provided the longest coverage. Obviously, this varies with insurance plan, so call the insurance plans involved and discuss your specific case at the start of therapy.

What if my identified client is a dependent child, covered by both parents' plans?

Again, this varies by the company. One insurance company representative I spoke with stated that if both parents are the primary subscribers on their own coverage, the plan of the parent whose birthday falls earlier in the year (remember, not necessarily the older parent) is the primary. If the parents have the same birthday, the primary plan may be the one who has provided coverage longer, or to the plan of the parent whose first name begins with an earlier alphabet letter! I am not making this up. Some plans may simply have the father as the primary carrier. However, this might not be the case if the parents are divorced or separated, where benefits are typically first billed to the custodial parent's plan first, and in cases of joint custody, the birthday rule typically applies. Now you see why you must call the plans involved in your case.

If I provide couples therapy, can I bill both partners' insurance for an individual therapy session?

No. The procedure codes are different (90847 vs. 90834). This would be misrepresenting the service provided, which is insurance fraud. This might also seem as if you are trying to collect your full fee from each plan, which is also fraud. You may bill both insurance plans for the same couples therapy session, but you would need to bill the primary plan first, and the secondary insurance after the primary has paid. You must also include on the claim the details about the other partner's coverage, as described on Pages 62-63, and Page 106. For more on insurance fraud, see Chapter 16.

What if the primary plan has a copayment of $25 and no deductible, and the secondary plan has a copayment of $35. Which do I collect?

After determining which plan is primary, follow the terms of this coverage. In this case, that means you would collect the $25 copayment. However, Jack may be able to seek reimbursement of this $25 from his secondary plan. See the chart earlier in this Chapter.

What if the client has a deductible for either plan?

If there is a deductible on either plan, you should still handle the claims submission in the same way. However, the plan may not pay unless he has used up the deductible, so if you are a network provider you should collect your contracted rate for the sessions until the deductible is exhausted. Submitting your claim will help the client to use up the deductible, and you (or the client) still need to submit the claim so that you can get the Explanation of Benefits (EOB), which you need if you are seeking reimbursement from the secondary plan.

Are there situations when I can get paid more than my contracted amount with either plan?

No. As you can see from the examples on Page 107 and 108, if you have a contract with either plan, and you have agreed to accept a discount as part of that contract, you may not receive more than your contracted rate for the session.

This sounds like a lot of work. Can I just collect the copayment or co-insurance from my client, bill the primary insurance company, and leave it to Jack to try to collect from his secondary insurance plan?

As it shows in the examples on Page 107 and 108 you may do this if you are NOT a network provider with the secondary plan. If you are a network provider for the secondary plan, you contract probably requires you to bill the plan on behalf of the client, even if you are out-of-network with the primary.

If you are not responsible for billing the secondary plan, you may educate Jill about the process and give her the necessary documentation to submit, including a copy of the EOB from the primary insurance showing what they paid for the sessions. Be sure she gets the proper claim form from their employer or insurance plan (or help them fill out the CMS-1500).

This seems incredibly complicated!

You get no argument here. Sometimes, this makes the idea of having a mental health billing service (one that is knowledgeable about this area) very attractive. But having to bill two insurance plans may not happen as often as you may think. And rest assured: In my mind this is the most complicated aspect of working with insurance. If you understand this, everything else will be a cake-walk. In fact, if you understand this, you know more than most insurance claims examiners!

18

Life as a Network Provider

೮೮ ೮ಾ

What's Expected of You

While expectations vary from network to network, here are some expectations I've found to be fairly universal among insurance plans:

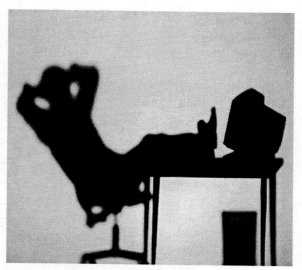

► **Return client calls promptly,** usually within one business day. "One of the biggest complaints we get from clients is that providers never call them back, even established clients," one insurance network manager shared.

► **Coordinate care with other treating professionals and the primary care physician.** Insurance plans are pushing coordination of care more than ever. Discuss the importance of this communication with each client. Make every reasonable attempt to obtain the client's signed release, and always record evidence of this coordination of care. This is especially important if the client is taking psychiatric medications, has a significant medical condition or substance abuse disorder, has a major mental illness, is violent, has difficulty following doctor's recommendations, or was referred to you by a medical practitioner. Value Options health plan reports coordination of care is one of the most commonly missing areas in its audits of provider documentation.[51]

► **If treating a child or adolescent, involve parents in treatment, and contact the child's school, when possible.**

► **Let the insurance company know about any changes** in your office address, phone numbers, specialty, tax ID numbers, or name.

► **Send the insurance company copies of your license and malpractice insurance renewals.** Be sure you do not let either lapse even briefly during treatment.

► **Let the insurance company know if you will be unable to take referrals** for any period of time due to vacation, leave, a full practice, or personal issues.

► **Keep your records in a professional manner, and make sure they are legible and secure.** There are many requirements in the area of what must be covered in your notes, and most large insurance companies will give you a list of what is required by their plan. This may include the client's name and ID number on each page, and your signature and credentials after every clinical entry, in ink, dated, and in chronological order. You may be asked to include in the chart demographic data, presenting problem, psychological and medical history, a mental status exam, diagnosis, treatment plan with measurable goals, releases, evidence of coordination of care with other treating providers, and information on past and present risk factors and use of cigarettes, drugs, and alcohol. This documentation is even a good idea for out-of-network providers, since whenever a client requests reimbursement from an insurance plan, your records may be requested by the plan.

► **Don't speak negatively to the client about the insurance plan.** Don't complain about the fee discount, whine about the plan's customer service, or in any way bad-mouth the insurance company. In the contract you signed with the plan, you may have even agreed not to criticize the company to the member. In addition, it is not professional, and may come back to haunt you if the client repeats your comments to the insurance company. I once foolishly told a potential client I was not taking new clients from her plan while I renegotiated my fee, which I felt was too low. The client repeated my remarks to her insurance company, and I got a scolding call from the plan the next day.

► **Don't "balance-bill" clients** for fees in excess of your contracted rate. This is a violation of your contract as a plan provider.

► **Don't tell clients, "my insurance slots are full, but I can see you for full fee."** You can't use the insurance plan as a source for filling your private-pay practice.

► **Leave emergency instructions on your answering machine or voicemail greeting.** If you have no answering service, instructing clients to go to an emergency room or dial 911 will usually meet the insurance company's requirement.

Resigning

If you resign, you are ethically and often contractually obligated to give as much advance notice as possible, both to the health plan and to affected clients. Most contracts require at least 30 days notice, but some require 90 days, so plan ahead. Your resignation must typically be in writing; it's wise to send it by certified mail so you have proof of sending it. Call the plan to ask where to send your resignation, and ask them to hold new referrals.

If you are seeing members of that plan in therapy, you may want to wait until their treatment is complete to resign, but once again, tell the plan to hold new referrals. I recommend you give a letter to all clients who are affected by your resignation, announcing the effective date that you will no longer be a network provider, outlining what this means for them, and what their options are. Document that you've given them this letter and keep a copy in their chart. You are ethically bound to transition your clients in a professional manner, and to collaborate in their referral. If you wish to continue seeing the member without their insurance, your contract may require you to continue providing services at the contracted rate until treatment is completed or until the client has been safely transitioned to another provider. This isn't common, but check your contract.

Provider-Profiling

In its broadest definition, "provider-profiling" refers to the type of information a managed care company keeps on its providers. However, to many providers it calls to mind the concept of something more sinister: The sense that Big Brother is looking over our shoulder with a clipboard.

What is in a provider profile? The information differs at each managed care company, and the companies don't like to say what information they keep on file. The information may include client complaint and client satisfaction data, clinical quality/outcomes data, utilization data (e.g., the average number of sessions per case, possibly even per diagnosis), the results of appointment accessibility surveys, and the results of site visit evaluations and treatment record reviews that may have taken place.

While this may be a thing of the past, there's also an informal sort of 'provider profiling' which may go on among managed care employees. Case managers who your read treatment requests sessions and intake coordinators who refer clients to you may remember their contact(s) with you and your treatment requests. This is yet another incentive for being friendly, kind, and professional to insurance company phone personnel, regardless of your frustration level.

Feeling paranoid? Don't panic. Insurance companies recognize that some clients have more severe problems than others, not all clients are going to love you, and that some clients are just plain difficult. They are looking for repeating patterns that are outside the expectations they have of providers (such as treatment requests that are always vague or lacking appropriate goals, or if your average length of treatment is unusually long, or your number of sessions per week or month is abnormally high).

Audits and Site Visits

From time to time, insurance companies are required to visit providers and audit (review) the files to be sure records are being kept in a professional manner, to review a case for a reimbursement decision, or to help maintain the quality of care.

Why would a plan ask for records?
- **A "medical necessity" review or appeal.** While plans don't usually ask for a full chart review, they could ask for information to help make a reimbursement or coverage decision based on Medical Necessity (For more about medical necessity, see Page 48)
- **An audit.** All insurance plans are required to pick a certain number of providers each year and conduct a review of their office procedures and files for quality control and improvement. These visits also allow them to check out your office, your policies, your forms, and your understanding of their plan.

Why might I be selected for an audit? You may be chosen randomly, or you may be selected because of a client complaint, a concern about your practice, because you have a home office, you see clients in their homes, the plan has a concern about your claims, or because you are a "high-volume provider." What puts you in the ranks of a high-volume provider? Value Options Health Plan's criteria is "any practitioner or facility that serves twenty-five unique ... members within a year."[52] But you may never get audited, or you may go years between audits. <u>In my 22 years as an insurance provider for more than 20</u>

<u>networks, I have never been formally audited</u> (am I tempting the audit gods by publicizing that?).

How can I prepare? The good news is that an audit isn't a blind ambush. You can usually get a listing (sometimes in the provider manual) of what the insurance plan would like to see in your notes and charts, including documentation of assessment questions, diagnoses, medical information, risk factors, goals, interventions, and referrals. Larger insurance companies often have a copy of these requirements on their websites, and some even have an "audit checklist" so you know ahead of time what they would expect if they were ever to audit you. The company may even give you warning of the audit, and resend the list of requirements. While it is tempting to "clean up your files" (or write progress notes you never wrote) before a site visit, resist the urge. This is unethical, and you could be guilty of fraud.

Do I need the client's written consent for an audit? "It is best to get the client's written consent – states like California require a patient's written consent in order to review mental health records, even in an audit," says Dave Jensen, an attorney at the California Association of Marriage and Family Therapists.[53] And a client's signature on the CMS-1500 claim form may not be enough. "Mental health has a higher standard of privacy than medical, and this particular release has been challenged in court, since it does not measure up to release requirements outlined by HIPAA," says Jensen.

As was mentioned earlier, even if you are out-of-network and Jack submits your invoice, he is opening his files to possible evaluation by the health plan. But keep in mind that if you are a HIPAA-covered entity, your psychotherapy notes are protected from insurance plan audits, if you keep them separately from your other notes – no matter what the plan may tell you (for further details about the different types of notes, see Page 35).

So what should I do if I'm asked for records?
- ▶ Contact the plan. Find out what they want and why. If being audited, ask the plan for their audit checklist.
- ▶ Try to create middle ground. "Find a way to give them what they need but release as little as possible, and maintain confidentiality," says Jensen. "See if they will accept a summary."
- ▶ Get a written release from your client, or – if this is just a general audit -- see if the plan will accept a "redacted" copy of your records (where all identifying information has been crossed-out or deleted).
- ▶ Try to relax. While audits can be anxiety-provoking, many of the items they are looking for are just good practice (like having a client's emergency contact and medications listed in the chart), so it is a great opportunity to start some good charting habits.

Colleagues who have gone through audits tell me they are not the hellish encounters they dreaded. This may be because the goal of the audit is quality improvement, not punishment. For example, United Behavioral Health has established a passing performance goal of 85 percent of expectations fulfilled.[54] And if you don't pass, they'll typically give you feedback about improvements they would like to see, if needed, and give you a chance to change your ways.

Network providers may also get a phone call from the state Department of Health or the Department of Insurance. Don't panic. They are likely calling simply to verify your demographic information and insurance network participation. They are often just confirming the accuracy of information given to them by insurance companies to be sure these plans have been truthful with them about their provider list, and have fulfilled certain requirements. You only need to return the call and answer a few basic questions, and they'll be happy.

If You'd Like More Clients

There are innumerable creative ways to increase referrals and market your practice. Here are a few that are unique to the insurance world:

- **Call the insurance company and ask about your current network status.** See if there has been a computer "glitch" that has kept you from getting more referrals. You may have been accidentally removed from the network or placed into "limbo-listing." This is when you have not been terminated from the network, but you have somehow lost your active status, perhaps because you failed to update some paperwork.

- **Is your information current?** Call the insurance company's provider relations or network management department to make sure your contact information, list of specialties, and address is up to date.

- **Check what prospective clients are seeing on the online provider directory at the company website.** If the insurance plan has a website, pretend you are a potential client, and see if you come up when you search the provider directory in your area. If so, are you listed as "active," or "taking new clients?" Is your other information correct? Also, does the site offer the opportunity to post a provider profile, listing your specialties or a personal statement? Some companies (like CIGNA) allow you to provide a provider profile and personal statement to describe your practice and your treatment philosophy in your own words. Use this space to sell yourself. Get feedback on your profile. Upload a picture, if possible.

- **Tell the plan if you are able to provide special services.** Some insurance companies will make more referrals (or even pay incentives) to therapists willing to see clients in special situations, such as Crisis Stabilization / emergency referrals, or accepting new clients who are about to be discharged from the hospital. Being able to provide Critical Incident Stress Debriefings (CISD) or teach employer-requested trainings or lectures might also get you referrals. You might also tell the plan if you are available on weekends, a much-needed service.

- **On your practice website and in other advertising, state that you accept insurance – you might even list the plans you accept.** I have found this to be amazingly effective. If Jack is choosing between you and other providers, and already knows you accept his insurance, you may be the first one called.

- **Create your own website where potential clients can learn more about you.** Recent research indicates over 70 percent of clients now search for professional services online first to help them choose which one to call.[55] This means that no matter where Jack gets your name (even if he gets it from your insurance plan's website), he is likely to enter your name into his Internet search engine to locate, research, and compare you with other therapists whose names are on his list. If he can't find you, or your website is just ho-hum, he will likely go on to the next name, and you will have lost a client. So it is essential to have your own dynamic website where a client can not only learn about your specialties and fees, but "hear your voice," and get a feeling for what it will be like to be in the room with you. I can't stress this enough.

▶ **Get more training.** Adding a specialty to your bag of tricks can increase referrals. Becoming a Certified Employee Assistance Professional (CEAP) might help you get on EAP plans and get EAP referrals, if this is an issue. In addition, one CIGNA Behavioral Health representative suggested that obtaining a Substance Abuse Professional (SAP) qualification (as defined by the Department of Transportation) could increase referrals. Learning to conduct therapy in a second language (including sign-language) is of course also helpful.

▶ **Distribute referral lists – including the insurance you accept -- to area physicians, hospitals, clinics, and other therapists.** For example, the therapists in my building all have a shared referral list, where we can instantly see each other's specialties, hours, fees, and who among us is a provider for any given network. This has proved a very effective referral tool for all of us.

▶ **Be sure you are on the list for all the company's plans.** Perhaps you joined the CureQuick PPO plan but were not automatically placed on the HMO or EAP network provider list.

▶ **Consider adding groups** that insurance plans might be seeking, and advertise them to the insurance plans.

▶ **The no-brainer:** Call and ask the insurance company what you might do to get more referrals.

If You'd Like to Halt the Flow

To temporarily stop the flow of insurance clients, call the provider relations department and ask them to put you on "inactive status," meaning that they won't refer to you for a period of time. When you would like to begin receiving referrals again, contact them to be sure you are again placed on "active" status. While this is fine for temporary periods, if you go on inactive status for too long you might get a call from the insurance plan, as they don't want you on the panel if you aren't going to be open for members.

19

"Should I Accept Insurance?"

ഇൽ ഈ

A Self-Quiz

Here are some questions to help you evaluate whether to join a network:

1. **What are your practice goals?** What kinds of clients do you like working with? How often would you like to be able to see them? Can the population you want to work with afford to pay you out of pocket for this amount of sessions per month? If not, what options do you have for enabling these clients to see you, and how do you feel about the other options?

2. **What are your income needs?** How many hours a week do you plan to work, and how much do you need to make? You may decide you can't afford to discount your fee in order to join a network, even for a few insurance clients.

3. **What is your cash flow situation?** Can you handle waiting several weeks after a session for insurance payments?

4. **Is private-pay-only working for you?** If you have a number of empty therapy slots you'd like to fill, accepting insurance might be worth considering. Becoming a network provider may bring a steady stream of referrals, which may be very helpful in building or filling out your practice. Perhaps you'd rather collect $60-$75 for an insurance client than collect nothing for an unfilled hour.

5. **How do you feel about advertising?** Do you loathe self-promotion? Have you been doing advertising, and it hasn't helped as much as you would like? Is it costing you more than you want to spend? If any of these is true for you, becoming a network provider can cut down on your need to advertise. As a

preferred provider, insurance plans put your name on their provider lists on their websites, and they give out your name to their members who call for referrals. I currently get three to four calls a day from clients who got my name from their insurance plan, which has significantly reduced my need to do outside advertising – other than a professional website, which is essential (review my argument for this, Page 117).

6. **Are you losing clients because they need to choose a provider on their plan?** Accepting insurance can mean retaining clients you enjoy working with, and not being forced to turn away new clients who need to use their benefits.

7. **What's your attitude toward managed care?** Evaluate your countertransference. Would you resent the idea of a case manager calling to discuss a case, or the idea of submitting a request for more sessions? Would you be tempted to speak negatively to your clients about managed care, your reimbursement rate, and your participation? Would you feel like a victim of managed care? If after reading this manual you are still very negatively inclined toward managed care, you might want to stay away from participation with any HMO plans, which have a higher level of oversight, and maybe even any provider networks.

8. **What is your attitude toward short-term therapy?** While it isn't necessary to restrict yourself to short-term therapy, this is the heart and soul of managed care, and you need to be comfortable with this work, at least much of the time. If you enjoy doing in-depth psychoanalysis with your client several times a week, working within a managed care framework may not be right for you.

9. **What level of involvement might work for you?** It may be helpful to review Chapter 2, which discussed the different types of insurance plans, and your options for participation. How do you feel about the idea of becoming involved with each type of plan? You might start out slowly, by joining one plan, just to see how this feels. Then perhaps you could consider whether to join additional networks. Remember, you can always resign any network should you choose not to continue.

10. **Are you reasonably organized?** While you don't need to be obsessive-compulsive to be a good managed care provider, organization is important. Claims must be filed in a timely manner, you must keep track of claims payments to be sure none slip between the cracks, and you have to keep on top of authorization numbers, expiration dates, and amount of sessions used. I also keep a folder for each plan, where I keep copies of the contract and any important correspondence. In this way you can also keep track of your contracted rate with each plan, claims addresses, contact information, and at have the basics of what each expects from you at your fingertips. This may sound daunting at first, but most providers quickly devise their own organization system (see Sample Service Record, Page 147).

11. **Do you keep good case notes and records?** Or at least, are you willing to start? While this is important for all therapists (and mandated by many state laws and/or professional ethical standards), it is doubly important for insurance providers because of the possibility of insurance plan audits or medical necessity review.

12. **Do you resent paperwork?** At the very minimum, working as a network provider will mean submitting claim forms. At the most, you may be providing

clients with HIPAA privacy policies, statements of understanding (treatment agreements provided by the insurance plan) questionnaires required by the plan, and filling out treatment authorization requests, recredentialing paperwork, and claims. You will also need to keep track of the insurance plan's coverage details for each client, and keep track of EOBs and claims payment. If you hate paperwork, you may choose not to take insurance, or simply avoid those plans with high paperwork requirements, limit the number of insurance clients you accept, or only take insurance as an out-of-network provider. Or you might hire a billing service to do some of this for you.

Don't try to fit into a "shoe that doesn't fit." Taking insurance is not for everyone.

Taking Care of Yourself: The Secrets of Managed Care Sanity

I'd be lying if I said that working with insurance is an easy path. Most things in life get more complicated when a third party is involved, and therapy is no different. However, if you do choose to become an insurance provider, here are a few self-care tips:

- ▶ **Balance your managed care and private-pay clients.** Belonging to too many insurance plans can mean that a high percentage of your clients are insurance clients. Too many insurance clients can mean you are not collecting your full fee often enough. If your therapy slots are filled by insurance clients, you may end up taking an uncomfortable income cut due to the high number of discounted rates. Also, the more insurance clients you have, the more time you spend doing paperwork and on the phone unsnarling claim problems.

- ▶ **Avoid reacting to those who bad-mouth insurance providers.** There is an unspoken attitude you may experience from some therapists who have a private-pay-only practice. That sentiment goes something like, "I'm a real therapist – I'm not selling out our profession to managed care." Or "I don't accept managed care because I know I am worth my fee -- insurance providers must not feel they deserve their full fee." Take a few deep breaths, and don't internalize these attitudes.

- ▶ **If you suspect a client is unhappy with you,** call the case manager and report what happened, so the plan has your side of the story in case the client complains.

- ▶ **Consult with other managed care providers.** Having regular consultation is recommended for all therapists, but I recommend it even more for those doing managed care. There are unique ethical, emotional, and clinical challenges involved with being a managed care provider, and it is helpful to have the support of other therapists familiar with these challenges.

▶ **Don't allow resentment about the fees to affect your work.** Get what support you need to make peace with the fees, or request a "raise" (see next page).

▶ **Consider resigning if the resentment is too great.** Contact the plan to find out their resignation policies, and how much advance notice you need to give (it may be as much as 90 days), where and how you should mail your resignation letter, and other details about transitioning your clients (for more on resignations, see Page 114).

Getting a Raise

It's no secret: The low reimbursement rate is our biggest complaint about working with insurance. Despite this, most therapists have never asked for a raise, assuming it would be a waste of time. And it's true that keeping provider fees down is the primary way managed care companies control costs and make profits. Yet providers are often able to negotiate raises - even in tough economic times. Over the years I have been able to negotiate several raises for myself, and I have been able to help therapists to get raises. So what have you got to lose?

▶ **Call the plan's Provider Relations Department** and ask how to go about making your request. Be prepared to defend why you feel you deserve a raise, in case they want to discuss it on the call.

▶ **You will typically be asked to write a letter.** Let them know why you are worth paying a bit more to keep. Include how long you have been with the network, whether you are a high-volume provider, and your unique specialties or skills, for example, if you can offer therapy in another language, crisis stabilization or emergency care, employer training or lectures, Critical Incident Stress Debriefings, inpatient pre- and post-discharge visits, home visits, weekend hours, or if you treat kids, Autism/Aspergers, ADHD, veterans, the hearing impaired, if you have experience with chemical dependency, trauma, chronic pain/illness, or if you are a Certified Employee Assistance Professional (CEAP) or Substance Abuse Professional (SAP). Raises might also be considered if an employer specifically requests your inclusion, if you work in an underserved area, if you are non-white or a male (plans need a diverse therapist base) or if you are part of a group practice that can offer a continuum of services. But don't assume if you have a general practice you can't get a raise (see "Letters of Interest" Page 22 for other ideas of what to highlight).

▶ **List the CPT codes for your services and the rates you are requesting for each.**

▶ **Avoid the biggest mistake: whining** about your costs and economic realities, or sounding resentful. You may want to briefly mention how long you have been on the network without a raise, but for the most part be positive, and just sell yourself.

▶ **Don't threaten to quit** if you don't get what you want. You may, however, hint you are unsure if you can continue at the current rate.

▶ **Find out where to send the letter,** whether you can fax it, and to whom you should address it.

► **You may want to hire an insurance consultant** to help you craft your rate request, and tailor it to your specific situation (see Resources, Page 133).

► **If you are unsuccessful, try again in six months.** Ask the plan if there is anything you might do to earn a fee increase.

► <u>**However, don't pick up the picket signs.**</u> Self-employed health care professional cannot collectively bargain for better contracts or better reimbursement rates – only therapists who are employees and who hold non-managerial positions can organize a union to collectively negotiate. Therapists who are self-employed are independent contractors, and cannot boycott or "strike," or threaten as a group to resign if reimbursement rates are not increased. This is considered "price fixing" or "restraint of trade," and violates the Sherman Antitrust Act of 1890.[56] The health plan needs only to establish that there has been some sort of "contract, combination, or conspiracy" between you and other healthcare professionals in an effort to collectively bargain and control reimbursement rates. "Such an agreement does not need to be in writing or be part of a formal agreement. A simple, informal discussion between competing [providers] at a social function expressing dissatisfaction about an HMO's payment schedule, followed by a....withdrawal of [providers] from an HMO could support a successful antitrust prosecution."[57] Even comparing reimbursement rates over coffee with a group of therapists or participating in a listserve or chatroom conversation to brainstorm what actions could be taken to affect reimbursement rates could potentially put you in hot water. This may trigger an investigation, especially if the health plan sees a number of therapists taking the same action. If the health plan can prove that there was some meeting, communication, or agreement between the therapists involved, the consequences can be severe. This is a felony, and the Act states that "...if convicted, you "shall be punished by a fine not exceeding...$350,000, or by imprisonment not exceeding three years, or both."[58]

Many providers are frustrated that their professional organizations do not actively fight plans for raises on their behalf. This is why they can't.

A Final Question

Barbara, knowing what you know now, would you still become as involved with insurance?

I am often asked this question. When I look back now on many important decisions I've made in my life, such as getting married, buying a house, starting a family, and even writing a book, I'm glad I didn't know how much work each would entail before I started. Perhaps then I would not have embraced them so fearlessly and optimistically, or would have steered away from them completely.

If I had read a book like this before I got involved in managed care, would it have seemed too complicated or too daunting? Probably so. But every payoff has its price. Just because something can be frustrating doesn't mean it should be avoided.

Success in working with insurance requires vision and balance. It helps to have a clear vision of what you want for yourself in your life and from your practice, and it is important to balance the number of private-pay and managed care clients to achieve that vision. As I said earlier, joining too many plans can lead to a situation where you are forced to accept discounted rates for their members, even for those clients who could have paid your full fee if you had not joined the network. Too many managed care clients can mean working twice as hard for the same pay, leave you ripe for resentment about paperwork and fee discounts, and leave no room in your practice for private-pay clients when they contact you.

However, as I said in the beginning of this tome, I am committed to finding ways to keep my services affordable to the people who may need them most, not just the most affluent among us. Not only has my managed care participation helped shield me from income fluctuations that can come from empty therapy hours, and provided me with a steady stream of clients, I have found it to be a wonderful way of keeping my door open to interesting and diverse clients from all walks of life. I challenge all of you who are reading this to find ways to make what we do more financially accessible to a wider range of people.

So I firmly believe that – even knowing what I know now -- I would still choose to become involved in managed care.

But ask me again tomorrow. Depending on the day's insurance frustrations, I might have a different answer!

Endnotes

ࡥ

1. Mary Riemersma, "The Typical California MFT: 2010 CAMFT Member Practice and Demographic Survey," *The Therapist* (July/August, 2010), [online], accessed April 5, 2014, http://viewer.zmags.com/publication/55bd5967#/55bd5967/30.
2. "Total Health Services Median and Mean Expenses per Person with Expenses and Distribution of Expenses by Source of Payment, United States, 2010," Medical Expenditure Panel Survey, Agency for Healthcare Research and Quality, U.S. Dept. of Health and Human Services, [online], accessed April 4, 2014, http://tinyurl.com/d8pnk8q
3. "Fee, Practice, and Managed Care Survey: New Data Shows that Most Clinicians are Falling Further Behind." *Psychotherapy Finances* (January, 2006), p. 1.
4. Casey Truffo, from a posting on *Psychologytoday.com* online bulletin board, June 1, 2006 (used with permission).
5. "Assisting an EAP Member in Crisis," *MHN News You Can Use* (Spring, 2006), p. 4.
6. Value Options Provider Manual, Appendix 5, Employee Assistance Program Handbook, 2013 -2014, [online]accessed April 5, 2014, http://www.valueoptions.com/providers/Handbook/ValueOptions_Provider_Handbook_Appendix_5.pdf
7. Value Options Provider Credentialing Criteria Checklist, [online], accessed April 4, 2014, http://www.valueoptions.com/providers/Forms/Administrative/Provider_Credentialing_Criteria_Checklist.pdf
8. Managed Health Network Recredentialing paperwork 2006 (author's copy).
9. United Behavioral Health EAP Clinician Prescreening Questionnaire, [online], accessed April 5, 2014, https://www.ubhonline.com/html/forms/pdf/eapPrescreeningQues.pdf
10. EAPA Guidelines, quoted in "Following are a Few FAQs...," *MHN News You Can Use* (Spring, 2005), p. 2.
11. Value Options Employee Assistance Program Statement of Understanding and Authorization to Release Information, author's copy, received April 6, 2008.
12. NCQA Standards, quoted in "Access and Availability," *Blue Cross Behavioral Health Network News* (Winter, 2005) p. 1.
13. "Fee, Practice, and Managed Care Survey: New Data Shows that Most Clinicians are Falling Further Behind." *Psychotherapy Finances* (January, 2006), p. 3.
14. "Should You Pay $100 to Join a Self-Described PPO?" *Psychotherapy Finances* (November 2005), p. 12.
15. "Standards, Audit Tool for Clinician Home Offices Established," *United Behavioral Health Network Notes* (Spring 2005), p. 10.
16. David Jensen, "Are You A Covered Entity?" Updated August 2010 [online]; accessed April 5,2013, http://www.camft.org/AM/Template.cfm?Section=Home&template=/CM/HTMLDisplay.cfm&ContentID=7539
17. Phone conversation with Michael Griffin, staff attorney, California Assn. of Marriage and Family Therapists, September 17, 2007.
18. U.S. Dept. of Health and Human Services, "Health Information Privacy Enforcement Highlights (As of August 31, 2013)", [online]; accessed April 5, 2014, http://www.hhs.gov/ocr/privacy/hipaa/enforcement/highlights/08312013.html

19. Wikipedia, "Patient Protection and Affordable Care Act," [online]; accessed April 5, 2014, http://en.wikipedia.org/wiki/Patient_Protection_and_Affordable_Care_Act

20. Legislative Counsel, State of California. "Confidentiality of Medical Information Act: California Civil Code, Section 56.10" [online]; accessed April 5, 2014, http://irb.ucsd.edu/CMIA.pdf

21. American Medical Association, *Current Procedural Terminology 2013 Standard Edition* (Chicago: American Medical Association Press, 2012).

22. Susan Frager, *Successful Private Practice: Winning Strategies for Mental Health Professionals* (New York: Wiley, 2000), p. 133.

23. American Medical Association, *AMA Physician's ICD-9-CM 2012: International Classification of Diseases* (Chicago: American Medical Association Press, 2011)

24. American Psychiatric Association, *Diagnostic and Statistical Manual of Mental Disorders* (American Psychiatric Publishing, Washington, D.C.) http://www.psychiatry.org/publications

25. Frager, *Successful Private Practice*, p. 152.

26. Frager, *Successful Private Practice*, p. 107.

27. EMDR International Association website, Insurance Information page [online]; accessed April 4, 2014, http://www.emdria.org/displaycommon.cfm?an=1&subarticlenbr=155

28. Brad Lotterman, quoted in *Psychotherapy Finances* (December, 2006).

29. American Medical Association, *Current Procedural Terminology 2013* (Chicago: American Medical Association Press, 2012).

30. National Uniform Claim Committee, "Insurance Claim Form Reference Instruction Manual for Form Version 02/12," Version 9.0, July, 2013, [online]; accessed April 5, 2014, http://www.nucc.org/images/stories/PDF/claim_form_manual_v9-0_7-13.pdf

31. American Medical Association, 2013 CPT Code Corrections Document (Errata) published December 12, 2012, [online]; accessed April 5, 2014, http://www.ama-assn.org/resources/doc/cpt/cpt-corrections-errata.pdf

32. Phone conversation with Kevin Petersen, Anthem Blue Cross case manager, May 24, 2011.

33. National Conference of State Legislatures, "State Coverage for Telehealth Services," [online]; accessed April 6, 2014; http://www.ncsl.org/research/health/state-coverage-for-telehealth-services.aspx

34. Phone conversation with Marlene Maheu, Ph.D, Executive Director, TeleMental Health Institute, February 20, 2013.

35. "Billing for Telephone Counseling or Non-Covered/Non-Certified Services, *United Behavioral Health Network Notes* (Spring 2005), p.6.

36. Correspondence from Value Options health plan to author, June 2006.

37. Michael Bihari, M.D., "Pre Existing Conditions - Understanding Exclusions and Creditable Coverage" updated April 15, 2010 [online]; accessed April 5, 2014, http://healthinsurance.about.com/od/healthinsurancebasics/a/preexisting_conditions_overview.htm

38. California HealthCare Foundation, "Ten Years of California's Independent Medical Review Process: A Look Back and a Prospectus for Change," January 2012 [online] accessed April 5, 2014, http://www.chcf.org/~/media/MEDIA%20LIBRARY%20Files/PDF/I/PDF%20IndependentMedicalReviewHistory.pdf

39. California Department of Managed Health Care, "Criteria for decision-making in Medical Necessity IMRs, California Dept of Managed Health Care," [online], assessed February 16, 2013, http://wp.dmhc.ca.gov/imr_info/info/6d.asp

40. Scott Barstow, The American Counseling Association, "The Affordable Care Act: What Counselors Should Know" [online]: accessed March 31, 2014 http://www.counseling.org/PublicPolicy/PDF/What_counselors_should_know-the_Affordable_Care_Act_12-12.pdf

41. Mary Riemersma, "Third Party Reimbursement," *The California Therapist* (March/April, 2001, updated July 2010 by Ann Tran) [online]; accessed April 5, 2014, http://www.camft.org/AM/Template.cfm?Section=Home&template=/CM/HTMLDisplay.cfm&ContentID=10553

42. "Fee Practice, and Managed Care Survey, Part III: What Clinicians are Doing about Credit Cards, Computers, etc.," *Psychotherapy Finances* (March 2006), p. 7.

43. Karen Rose, posting on East Bay Chapter, California Association of Marriage and Family Therapist's listserve, March 4, 2008 (used with permission).

44. "UBHonline Speeds Up Claims Processing," *United Behavioral Health Network Notes* (Fall 2005), p. 7.

45. California HealthCare Foundation, "California Healthcare Foundation, National Consumer Health Privacy Survey 2005, " [online]; accessed April 5, 2014, http://www.chcf.org/publications/2005/11/national-consumer-health-privacy-survey-2005

46. Susan Frager, quoted in "Managed Care: Strategies for Billing Insurance and MCOs for Marital Therapy," *Psychotherapy Finances* (November 2005), p. 2.

47. Mary Riemersma, "What is Insurance Fraud?" *The California Therapist*, (March/April 2001), updated December 2009 by Ann Tran, JD, [online]; accessed April 5, 2014, http://www.camft.org/AM/Template.cfm?Section=Home&template=/CM/HTMLDisplay.cfm&ContentID=10560

48. Michael Brandt, "Health Care Fraud Affects Everyone," *Health Net Physician News* (Spring 2000), p. 7.

49. Riemersma, "What is Insurance Fraud?"

50. Susan Frager, LCSW, e-mail to the author, April 8, 2008 (used with permission).

51. "Treatment Record Review Results: Are You Compliant?" *The Valued Provider* (Spring 2006), p. 6.

52. "Treatment Record Review Results: Are You Compliant?" *The Valued Provider* (Spring 2006), p. 6.

53. David Jensen, CAMFT attorney, phone conversation, March 2, 2011.

54. "Treatment Record Documentation Requirements," *United Behavioral Health Network Notes* (Fall 2005), p. 7.

55. Joe Bavonese, "How to Develop a Money Mindset," *Psychotherapy Networker,* [online];accessed April 5, 2014 http://www.psychotherapynetworker.org/component/content/article/83-2007-julyaugust/203-how-to-develop-a-money-mindset

56. "U.S. Department of Justice, Antitrust Division Manual, Chapter 2," [online]; assessed April 5, 2014, http://www.justice.gov/atr/public/divisionmanual/chapter2.pdf

57. Havins, Weldon, *Nevada Physician Legal Handbook*, Chapter 3 Antitrust, [online]; assessed September 19, 2011, http://www.whavins.com/nplh3.htm

58. "U.S. Dept of Justice Antitrust Division Manual, Chapter 2."

APPENDIX A

State Insurance Departments

ℬↄ ↄℬ

The contact information below is a place to start to get information about filing complaints about insurance plans, to appeal care or claim denials, or to request Independent (or external) treatment reviews. This information is from the website of each state's Department of Insurance (accessed April 5, 2014).

Alabama Department of Insurance
http://www.aldoi.gov
334-269-3550

Alaska Division of Insurance
http://www.dced.state.ak.us/ins
907-465-2518

Arizona Department of Insurance
http://www.id.state.az.us
800-325-2548 or 602-364-2499

Arkansas Department of Insurance
http://insurance.arkansas.gov
800-852-5494 or 501-371-2600

California Department of Insurance
http://www.insurance.ca.gov
800-927-4357 or 213-867-8921

► **California Department of Managed Health Care**
http://www.hmohelp.ca.gov
Provider's helpline: 877-525-1295
Consumer helpline: 888-HMO-2219

Colorado Division of Insurance
http://www.dora.state.co.us/insurance
303-894-7499

Connecticut Department of Insurance
http://www.ct.gov/cid/site/default.asp
800-203-3447 or 860-297-3900

Delaware Insurance Department
http://www.delawareinsurance.gov
302-674-7300

District of Columbia Department of Insurance
http://disr.washingtondc.gov/disr/site
202-727-8000

Florida Office of Insurance Regulation
http://www.floir.com
850-413-3140

Georgia Office of Insurance
http://www.inscomm.state.ga.us
800-656-2298 or 406-656-2070

Hawaii Department of Insurance
http://hawaii.gov/dcca/ins/
808-586-2790 or 2799

Idaho Department of Insurance
http://www.doi.idaho.gov
800-721-3272

Illinois Division of Insurance
http://insurance.illinois.gov
877-527-9431

Indiana Department of Insurance
http://www.in.gov/idoi
317-232-2385

Iowa Insurance Division
http://www.iid.state.ia.us/
877-955-1212

Kansas Insurance Department
http://www.ksinsurance.org/
800-432-2484

Kentucky Department of Insurance
http://insurance.ky.gov
800-595-6053 or 502-564-3630

Louisiana Department of Insurance
http://www.ldi.la.gov
800-259-5300 or 800-259-5301

Maine Bureau of Insurance
http://www.state.me.us/pfr/insurance
800-300-5000 207-624-8475

Maryland Insurance Administration
http://www.mdinsurance.state.md.us/
800-492-6116 x2458

Massachusetts Division of Insurance
http://www.mass.gov/doi
877-563-4467 or 617- 521-7794

- ► Office of Patient Protection:
  http://www.mass.gov/dph/opp
  800-436-7757
- ► Bureau of Managed Care:
  617-521-7372

Michigan Office of Financial and Insurance Regulation
http://www.michigan.gov/lara
877-999-6442

Minnesota Department of Health,
Managed Care Systems section
http://www.health.state.mn.us/divs/hpsc/mcs
651-201-5100 or 800-657-3916

Mississippi Insurance Department
http://www.mid.state.ms.us
800-562-2957 or 601-359-3569

Missouri Department of Insurance
http://insurance.mo.gov/
573-751-4126

Montana Insurance Division
http://sao.mt.gov
800-332-6148 or 406-444-2040

Nebraska Department of Insurance
http://www.doi.ne.gov
877-564-7323

Nevada Division of Insurance
http://doi.state.nv.us
775-687-0700 or 702-486-4009

New Hampshire Insurance Department
http://www.state.nh.us/insurance/
603.271.2261

New Jersey Department of Banking and Insurance
http://www.state.nj.us/dobi/
800-446-7467

- ► Office of Managed Care:
  609-292-7272

New Mexico Public Regulation Commission, Insurance Division, Managed Healthcare Bureau
http://www.nmprc.state.nm.us/id.htm
505-827-4601 or 800- 947-4722 or 888-4-ASK-PRC

New York State Department of Health Bureau of Managed Care
https://www.health.ny.gov/health_care/managed_care/complaints/
800-206-8125

North Carolina Department of Insurance
http://www.ncdoi.com
800-546-5664 or 919-807-6750

North Dakota Insurance Department
http://www.nd.gov/ndins/
800-247-0560 or 701-328.2440

Ohio Department of Insurance, Consumer Services Division
www.insurance.ohio.gov
800-686-1526 or 614- 644-2658

Oklahoma Insurance Department
http://www.ok.gov/oid/
800-522-0071 or 405-521-2828

Oregon Insurance Division
http://insurance.oregon.gov
503-947-7984 or 888-877-4894

Pennsylvania Insurance Department
www.ins.state.pa.us
877-881-6388 or 717-787-2317

Rhode Island Office of the Health Insurance Commissioner
http://www.ohic.ri.gov
401- 462-9517

South Carolina Department of Insurance
http://www.doi.sc.gov
803-737-6180 or 803-737-6160

South Dakota Division of Insurance
http://dlr.sd.gov/reg/insurance
605-773-3563

Tennessee Department of Commerce and Insurance, Consumer Insurance Services
http://www.tennessee.gov/commerce/ins urance
800-342-4029 or 615-741-2218

Texas Department of Insurance
http://www.tdi.state.tx.us
800-252-3439

Utah Insurance Department Health Insurance Division & Office of Consumer Health Assistance (OCHA)
http://www.insurance.utah.gov/
801-538-3077 or 800-439-3805

Vermont Department of Banking, Insurance, Securities, and Health Care Administration -- Division of Health Care Administration
http://www.bishca.state.vt.us
800-964-1784

Virginia State Corporation Commission, Bureau of Insurance Office of Managed Care Ombudsmen
http://www.scc.virginia.gov/boi/omb
877-310-6560

Washington D.C. *(see District of Columbia, Page 129)*

Washington Office of the Insurance Commissioner
http://www.insurance.wa.gov/
800-562-6900

West Virginia Offices of the Insurance Commissioner, Consumer Service Division
http://www.wvinsurance.gov/
888-879-9842

Wisconsin Office of the Commissioner of Insurance
http://oci.wi.gov/oci_home.htm
800-236-8517 or 608-266-3585

Wyoming Insurance Department
http://insurance.state.wy.us
800-438-5768 or 307-777-7401

Appendix B

Resources

Updated April 5, 2014

ஐ ௧௮

MENTAL HEALTH INSURANCE CONSULTANTS

Barbara Griswold, LMFT
Author of this book. Available to answer insurance questions, assist in applying to plans, preparing for treatment reviews, fighting denials, and give general practice-building advice. Send e-mail to subscribe to free e-mail newsletter.
4100 Moorpark Ave. Suite 116
San Jose, CA 95117
(408) 985-0846
www.theInsuranceMaze.com
BarbGris@aol.com

Susan Frager, LCSW, Billing Specialist
Expert consultant and biller
Psych Admin Partners billing service
(888)-530-9833
www.psychadminpartners.com
susan@psychadminpartners.com

Fran Wickner, PhD, MFT
Help getting on panels, general advice,
Sells mailing labels of insurers
1350-A Solano Avenue Suite #4
Albany, CA 94706
(510) 527-4011
www.franwickner.com
Franwickner@hotmail.com

Lynn Grodzki, LCSW
Private practice coach and author
910 La Grande Road
Silver Spring, MD 20903
(301) 434-0766
www.privatepracticesuccess.com
info@privatepracticesuccess.com

PROFESSIONAL ORGANIZATIONS

American Psychological Association
750 First Street, NE
Washington, DC 20002-4242
(800) 374-2721 or (202) 336-5500
www.apa.org

American Association of Marriage and Family Therapists
112 S. Alfred Street, Alexandria, VA 22314
(703) 838-9808
www.aamft.org

California Association of Marriage and Family Therapists
Great website articles & member hotline
7901 Raytheon Road
San Diego, CA 92111
(858) 292-2638
www.camft.org

Employee Assistance Professionals Association
4350 North Fairfax Dr., Suite 740
Arlington, Virginia 22203
(703) 387-1000
www.eapassn.org

National Association of Social Workers
750 First Street, NE, Suite 700
Washington, DC 20002-4241
(202) 408-8600
http://www.naswdc.org/

American Counseling Association
5999 Stevenson Ave.
Alexandria, VA 22304
(800) 347-6647
http://www.counseling.org

CMS-1500 Billing Forms

- *Be sure to buy latest version (at this writing, 02/12 version)*
- *Submitting claims on original red forms (NOT COPIES) can significantly speed payment*
- *Get "single-sheet laser" if you use a printer to print claims or handwrite but don't need a copy; order "2-part, continuous-feed carbonless duplicates" if you handwrite and want an instant copy*

www.theInsuranceMaze.com
Buy claim forms at author's website
Sold in batches of 100 forms
(408) 985-0846
Or contact Barbara at barbgris@aol.com
www.theInsuranceMaze.com

www.Staples.com
1-800-333-3330
www.Staples.com

National Uniform Claim Committee
Get more detailed line-by-line details on how to complete the claim form
www.nucc.org

National Provider Identifier (NPI)

National Plan and Provider Enumeration System (NPPES)
Apply for your NPI: The NPI Enumerator
P.O. Box 6059
Fargo, ND 58108-6059
(800) 465-3203
http://tinyurl.com/getnpi
customerservice@npienumerator.com

For more information about the NPI:
Centers for Medicare/Medicaid Services
7500 Security Boulevard
Baltimore, MD 21244
(877) 267-2323
http://tinyurl.com/npianswers

TeleHealth / Online Therapy

The Telehealth Institute
Marlene Maheu, Ph.D., Exec. Director
Consultations, classes in online therapy issues -- An expert in online therapy
1876 Horse Creek Road
Cheyenne, Wyoming 82009
619-928-2627, 619-255-2788
http://telehealth.org
info@telehealth.org,

- **For a list of states where telehealth is mandated to be paid:**
  http://telehealth.org/mandated-states

California Telehealth Network
2001 P St, Suite 100
Sacramento, CA 958111
855-385-5082
http://www.caltelehealth.org

Center for Telehealth and e-Health Law
P.O. Box 15850
Washington DC 20003
(202) 499-6970
info@ctel.org

Article: "State Coverage for Telehealth Services," by the National Conference of State Legislatures, [online]; accessed April 6, 2014
http://tinyurl.com/telehealthlaws

Employer Identification Numbers

Internal Revenue Service
Apply for EINs online, by phone, or fax IRS Form SS-4 to your local IRS office
Warning: *When switching from using a Social Security Number to an EIN, submit completed IRS Form W-9 to each plan. Check with plans before submitting claims to be sure they have your EIN in system. It is recommended you do this at the start of a calendar year for tax purposes.*
(800) 829-4933
http://tinyurl.com/getyourEIN or
www.irs.gov

INSURANCE BILLING RESOURCES

Office Ally
Offers FREE submission of claims to insurance plans, FREE online practice billing system (PracticeMate)
PO Box 872020, Vancouver, WA 98687
(360) 975-7000
www.officeally.com

Assessment Psychology Online
Listing of some major billing & practice management software and billers
www.assessmentpsychology.com/practice software.htm#links

California Association of Marriage and Family Therapists
Members can get a list of billing software programs from the website
7901 Raytheon Road
San Diego, CA 92111 - 1606
(858) 292-2638
www.camft.org

PARITY LAWS

National Alliance on Mental Illness
3803 N. Fairfax Dr., Suite 100
Arlington, VA 22203
 (800) 950-6264 or (703) 524-7600
www.nami.org

Mental Health America
2000 N. Beauregard St., 6th Floor
Alexandria, VA 22311
(800) 969-6642 or (703) 684-7722
www.nmha.org (search "parity")

Parity Implementation Coalition
For parity information or to report health plan parity violations; also get *"Parity Toolkit for Addiction & Mental Health Consumers, Providers, and Advocates -- Simplifying the Appeals Process: Strategies for Winning Disputes with Your Health Plan"*
101 Constitution Ave. NW Suite 675E
Washington, DC 20001
(866)882-6227
http://parityispersonal.org/

CODES: CPT Codes, Diagnosis Codes, and Place of Service Codes

The 2013 CPT Codes: What Every Therapist Should Know by Barbara Griswold, MFT
Author of this book has put together outline for therapists of major changes and subtle issues when it comes to billing insurance
(408) 985.0846
barbgris@aol.com
www.theInsuranceMaze.com/store/index.html

Current Procedural Terminology Codes
American Medical Association Bookstore
Orders: PO Box 930876
Atlanta, GA 31193-0876
(800) 621-8335
http://tinyurl.com/amabookstore

ICD (International Classification of Diseases – be sure you have the latest version)
American Medical Association Bookstore
Orders: PO Box 930876
Atlanta, GA 31193-0876
(800) 621-8335
http://tinyurl.com/amabookstore

icd9coding.com
Website where you can check diagnosis codes and to see if you have full number of digits (search for your code, red indicator tells you have all digits).
http://icd9coding.com

ICD and CPT Codes are available free from many professional associations

Place of Service Codes (POS)
Center for Medicare and Medicaid Services
http://tinyurl.com/placeofservice

DSM-5 Diagnostic and Statistical Manual of Mental Disorders 5th Edition)
American Psychiatric Publishing
1000 Wilson Boulevard, Suite 1825
Arlington, VA 22209
800-368-5777 or 703-907-7322
http://www.appi.org/Pages/DSM.aspx

HIPAA RESOURCES

U.S. Department of Health and Human Services
200 Independence Avenue, SW
Washington, D.C. 20201
 (866) 627-7748 (HIPAA toll-free)
www.hhs.gov/ocr/hipaa

Center for Medicare/Medicaid Services
7500 Security Boulevard
Baltimore, MD 21244
(877) 267-2323
http://www.cms.gov/Regulations-and-Guidance/HIPAA-Administrative-Simplification/HIPAAGenInfo/index.html

MANAGED CARE COMPANY LISTS

Many professional associations (including CAMFT) have a list of plans that operate in your state and their contact information

State Departments of Insurance may have such lists (see Page 129)

Fran Wickner, PhD, MFT
Sells list of over plans that operate in California, with contact information
1350-A Solano Avenue Suite #4
Albany, CA 94706
(510) 527-4011
www.franwickner.com (click on Private Practice Products)
franwickner@hotmail.com

HEALTH CARE REFORM AND THE AFFORDABLE CARE ACT

HealthCare.gov
A government website managed by the U.S. Centers for Medicare & Medicaid Services
7500 Security Boulevard
Baltimore, MD 21244
(800) 318-2596 (24 hours, 7 days/week)
www.healthcare.gov

RESOURCES FOR FINDING INSURANCE

Foundation for Health Coverage Education
Receive a personalized list of your health coverage options, get helpful information and pamphlets on insurance and COBRA
www.coverageforall.org
fhceinfo@coverageforall.org

Healthcare.gov Insurance Plan Finder
This web tool will help you find private insurance or public program options outside the marketplace plans, for individuals, families, and small businesses
A federal government website managed by the U.S. Department of Health & Human Services
200 Independence Avenue, S.W.
Washington, D.C. 20201
(800) 318-2596 (24 hours, 7 days/week)
http://finder.healthcare.gov/

Endorsement or recommendation of any of these resources is not implied, unless stated. Author cannot be held liable for the quality of service provided by any individual or agency on this list. Updated 4/5/4, but all information is subject to change.

APPENDIX C

Glossary

ಬಿ ಅ

Account: An agreement a managed care company may have with an employer, union, or government, (ex. "CureQuick offers their Premier HMO $15 Copayment plan to the Microsoft Employer account.") A care management team at the insurance company may be devoted to one account or employer group.

Ad hoc agreement: See Single case agreement.

Appeal: A process available to clients, their family members, their treating providers, or their representatives to request reconsideration of a previous denial of claim reimbursement, or previous denied request for a covered service or authorization for service (see Sample Appeal Letter, Page 84).

Audit: A review of a therapist's file on a particular client or group of clients by the health plan in order to assure quality of care and to be sure the therapist is following insurance procedures.

Authorization: See Pre-authorization

Balance-billing: This is when a provider charges the client the difference between the provider's full fee and their contracted rate with the insurance plan. Network providers may not bill clients for this difference – they have agreed in their contract to write this off.

Behavioral health care: Services for the assessment and treatment of mental health and/or substance abuse issues.

Benefit year: The coverage period, usually 12 months long, that is used for administration of a health benefits plan. Clients, for example, may have benefits for 20 sessions from January 1 through December 31 of any year, or they may have 20 sessions between July 1 of one year and June 30 of the next year.

Benefits: The portion of costs of services paid by a health plan. If the plan pays the remainder of a bill after an office copayment is made, the amount the plan paid is the benefit.

Care manager: See Case manager

Carrier: An insurance company is often referred to as the insurance carrier.

Carve-out: When a health insurance company has decided not to manage the mental health benefits for their members, they may instead "carved out" their mental health benefits, by signing a contract with another company to handle the mental health case management and/or claims payment.

Case manager: Case managers work for the insurance company, reviewing clients' care to make sure it is delivered in the most cost-effective manner. They authorize treatment requests and make network referrals when needed. Also called care managers.

CEAP: see Certified Employee Assistance Provider

Certification: See Precertification

Certified Employee Assistance Provider (CEAP): A health care professional who has gone through the additional training classes required to become a Certified Employee Assistance Provider.

CHAMPUS (Civilian Health and Medical Program of the Uniformed Services): A medical benefits program provided by the federal government.

Claim: A request for payment made to the health insurance plan from the client or the treating provider.

CMS-1500 (Centers for Medicare and Medicaid Services Form 1500): Formerly known as the HCFA-1500, this is a claim form that is accepted by most private and federal health insurance plans.

COBRA (Consolidated Omnibus Budget Reconciliation Act): A federal statute that requires employers to continue to offer coverage to employees and dependents who would otherwise have lost their insurance coverage for reasons specified in the statute (for example, loss of a job, disability, divorce, loss of dependent child status, employee death, etc.). They are given the opportunity to purchase or take over payment of the premiums for the same health benefits the employer provides to its remaining employees. Continuation of coverage is limited (usually 18 months for employees and dependents who would otherwise lose coverage due to loss of employment or work hour reduction, 29 months for disability-related events, or 36 months for dependents who would lose coverage for other reasons).

Co-insurance: The percentage of the fee that a client is responsible to pay (after his or her deductible has been met, if any). For example, if the health insurance company pays 80 percent of the claim, the client's co-insurance is 20 percent.

Continuity of care: When a client switches insurance plans, and the health plan allows (or is required by law to allow) clients to complete their care with their current healthcare provider, or to help them make a smooth transition to a network provider at their new insurance plan. In certain cases either the new or old health care may provide coverage (even with an out of network provider) until an acute phase of treatment is over.

Contract (subscriber's): A legal agreement between a member (the client or a family member) and the insurance plan that describes the benefits and limitations of the coverage.

Contract (provider's): A legal agreement between an individual treating provider and the insurance plan outlining the terms of their agreement to provide services to covered members.

Contracted rate, or contracted fee: The fee the insurance company will pay for a session, as outlined in the network provider contract. This is usually a discounted fee from the provider's usual full fee.

Coordination of benefits (COB): When a client has two or more insurance plans, the plans will coordinate the payment of the claim to see which plan is primary, to prevent overpayment/duplication.

Copayment (copay): The fixed, flat fee per visit that a client must pay for eligible expenses, after any deductible is met. The health insurance company pays the rest, up to the contracted rate.

Coverage: The benefits provided by the insurance plan – what services and diagnoses are covered, at what frequency, and at what rate.

Covered services: Those procedures the insurance company agrees to pay under the member's benefit contract. Most health insurance plans have limitations on their coverage.

CPT codes: The physician's Current Procedural Terminology codes, published by the American Medical Association, were developed to provide a universal language to describe medical and diagnostic services provided by health care providers.

Credentialing: A process used by an insurance company in which a health care provider's credentials are reviewed and matched against the credentials required to participate in the provider network.

Date of service (DOS): The date of the service or session that was provided to the client.

Deductible: The dollar amount that a client must pay yearly for eligible health services before his health plan begins paying. For example, a client with a $200 deductible will have to pay the first $200 of medical bills each year before insurance begins to cover the expenses. Not all plans have deductibles. Not all medical bills will be counted in full toward the deductible. During the deductible, network providers should charge clients their contracted amount and continue to submit claims.

Dependent: A person eligible for coverage under an employee benefits plan because of that person's relationship to an employee, including spouses, children, and adopted children.

Dispute: Also known as an appeal. A provider's written notice to the insurance company challenging, appealing, or requesting reconsideration of a claim that has been denied, adjusted, or contested, or disputing a request for reimbursement of an overpayment of a claim.

Dispute resolution: The process that each insurance plan has set up for handling and settling disputes.

DOS: See Date of service

Double (or duplicate) coverage: When a client has coverage under more than one health benefits plan (e.g., he is covered by insurance through both his employer and his wife's employer, or when a couple you are seeing both have their own plans).

DSM: *The Diagnostic and Statistical Manual of Mental Disorders*, published by the American Psychiatric Association, provides a common language and standard criteria for the diagnosis and classification of mental disorders.

EAP: See Employee assistance program, or employee assistance provider/professional.

EIN (Employer Identification Number): This is a type of Tax Identification Number (TIN) that any business (including therapists in private practice) can obtain from the Internal Revenue Service. The EIN can be used on claims and invoices in place of your Social Security Number.

Effective date: The date on which the client's coverage began under the health benefits plan.

Eligible services: Services are considered eligible or ineligible for coverage by the health benefits plan depending on the plan's provisions.

Employee assistance professional/provider: A clinician who has contracted with an employee assistance program (EAP) to provide counseling services which are free to the employee or dependent (see also "Employee assistance program").

Employee assistance program (EAP): An EAP is an assessment, referral and short-term counseling program that is paid for by some employers and is available for free to their employees and dependents as an employee benefit. An employer may hire EAP professionals that work onsite at the company, or may contract with clinicians in the community.

Employee Retirement Income Security Act (ERISA): A federal law that applies to retirement programs and to employee welfare benefit programs established or maintained by employers and unions. Because these plans are governed by ERISA, which is federal law, the federal law pre-empts state law, and thus self-insured benefit plans can avoid certain state mandates.

Employer Identification Number: see EIN

Enrollee: An individual who is enrolled and eligible for coverage under a health plan.

EOB: See Explanation of Benefits.

EPO (exclusive provider organization): A specific type of health plan similar to a PPO, except that the client does not have the option of choosing an out-of-network provider for reimbursable services. Plan members can visit specialists without a referral, and don't need to choose a primary care physician for coverage.

ERISA: See Employee Retirement Income Security Act

Exclusions: Specific conditions or services that are not covered under the plan's benefit agreement.

Exclusive provider organization: See EPO

Explanation of Benefits (EOB): Once a claim is made for services, an EOB is the statement provided by the health plan that accompanies the reimbursement check, and explains how the claim was processed. It may include the portion of the charges that went to satisfy the client's deductible or co-insurance, and any other adjustments made before it was paid. Or it may explain why no payment was made. A copy of the EOB goes to both the insured and the provider.

Fee-for-service plans: A healthcare plan in which providers receive payment based on their billed charges for each service provided without treatment review or authorization. These plans are not considered "managed care," and allow visits to any healthcare professional. See Indemnity plans.

Flexible spending account (FSA): An employer-sponsored tax-advantaged savings account that clients may use to pay medical and dependent care expenses from pre-tax dollars. Clients must say in advance how much they want to put in the account each year, and if not spent by year-end, it is lost.

HCFA-1500: See CMS-1500.

Health Insurance Portability and Accountability Act: see HIPAA

Health maintenance organization: See HMO

Health reimbursement account (HRA): These are tax-exempt accounts that many employers have paid into that employees may use specifically for the payment of health care expenses. Clients control the investments they make, the amount they deposit, and what expenses they pay.

Health savings account (HSA): These are tax-exempt accounts that many clients (and often their employers) have paid into that employees may use for the payment of health care expenses. Clients control the investments they make, the amount they deposit, and what expenses they pay. They are also required to have a high deductible health plan.

HIPAA (Health Insurance Portability and Accountability Act): This law addresses health insurance portability, and is designed to protect health insurance coverage for workers and their families when they change or lose their jobs. It is also aimed at reducing the administrative costs of providing health care through standardization, and includes requirements to protect the privacy of clients' health information. Health plans and many providers who transmit confidential health information electronically are required to follow the requirements of HIPAA.

HMO (health maintenance organization): A health plan that typically offers broader preventive coverage and lower out-of-pocket expenses for its members. Plan members are required to have a primary care physician, who coordinates care, and his/her referral may be required to see specialists. There is typically no annual deductible, and copayments are usually low. However, coverage is not available for out-of-network providers, except for emergency care.

HRA: See Health reimbursement arrangement

HSA: See Health savings account

ICD (International Classification of Diseases): Medical and psychiatric diagnostic codes developed by the American Medical Association, and now required by health insurers on claim forms.

Indemnity plan: A type of health benefits plan under which the covered person pays an annual deductible, and then the health benefit plan pays a percentage of covered charges. No primary care physician referral is required, no referrals are required for specialists, and there are no provider networks. The provider controls the type of treatment, length of treatment, and fee charged. Also called a fee-for-service plan.

Insured: The individual who is enrolled and eligible for coverage under a health plan.

Invoice: Also known as a statement or Superbill (see sample invoice Page 145). A list of charges and payments made for healthcare services provided. Out of network providers may give these to a client to submit to their insurance plan for reimbursement (network providers must bill for clients).

Legacy Identifiers: These are provider identification numbers other than the National Provider Identifier (NPI) used by a health plan to identify a provider. Examples include Provider Identification Numbers (PINS), Unique Physician Identification Numbers (UPINs) and state license numbers. Legacy Identifiers may still be accepted on claim forms by some insurance plans if a provider is not a HIPAA Covered Entity, in which case the provider is required to use a NPI

Lifetime maximum/limit: The cap placed on the benefits paid under an insurance policy during a client's lifetime. Due to the Affordable Care Act, most plans no longer have these limits.

Managed care: A system of health care delivery that is designed to manage the cost, use and quality of the health care, and typically offers financial incentives for clients to use the providers who belong to the plan's provider network. Managed care may include pretreatment authorization, session limits, utilization review, and provider discounts. Examples include HMO, PPO, EPO, and POS plans.

Medical necessity: The health plan's determination that there is a medical need for treatment, that the course of treatment is the most appropriate for the symptoms the client is experiencing, is provided within generally accepted standards of practice, and is not rendered primarily for the convenience of the client or provider.

Medical savings account (MSA): See Health savings account

Member: The individual or dependent who is enrolled in and eligible for coverage under a health plan.

MH/SA: An abbreviation used by insurers to refer to Mental Health and Substance Abuse benefits. Do not confuse with MHSA, which can mean "Mental Health Service Administrators" indicating there may be a carve-out of mental health benefits to another plan, a "mental health service administrator."

National Provider Identifier (NPI): As part of HIPAA laws, The Centers for Medicare and Medicaid Services (CMS) will be assigning all HIPAA providers ("covered entities") unique provider identification numbers to use when billing and communicating with all private and government health plans.

Network: A group of health care providers under contract with a managed care company. They may agree to accept discounts, file claims, and permit their treatment to be reviewed.

Network provider: Any health care provider who has entered into an agreement with a managed care plan, and thus belongs to the insurance plan's network of providers. Choosing a network provider gives the member the advantage of discounted fees, having claims filed on their behalf, and often better coverage by the health plan. Also called a participating provider.

NPI: see National Provider Identifier

Open enrollment: A period when eligible persons can enroll in a new health benefit plan for the next benefit year.

Out-of-network provider: Any health care provider that does not belong to the insurance plan's network. Many insurance plans (including PPO and POS plans) cover visits to out-of-network providers, but often at a lower reimbursement rate.

Out-of-pocket expenses: Copayments, deductibles, or fees paid by clients for health services.

Out-of-pocket maximum: The most money a client will be required to pay per year before the plan begins to pay 100 percent of covered health expenses. This does not include the payment of regular premiums. In some plans, the client may still have to pay copayments.

Panel: The network of providers who have contracted with a health care plan to provide services to the insurance members or enrollees. Also known as the provider network.

Parity: State or federal laws which require insurance companies to grant some measure of equality between the benefits they provide for mental health and medical visits.

Participant: A person who is eligible to receive benefits under a health benefits plan. This may refer to the employee, spouse, or other dependents.

Participating provider: Any health care provider that has entered into an agreement with a managed care plan, and thus belongs to the insurance plan's network of providers. Choosing a participating provider (network provider) gives the member the advantage of discounted fees, not having to file their own claims, and often a higher level of coverage by the health plan. Also called a network provider.

Pass-through: Some health plans allow a certain number of visits with a provider before authorization for treatment is needed. These are sometimes called "pass-through sessions."

Payer: An insurance company, self-funded employer, union or employer trust, managed care plan, state or federal government agency which has entered into a contractual arrangement to pay for health services for a client or member.

PCP: See Primary care physician

Pended claim: A claim that has been delayed because it requires additional information before it can be processed. This often involves waiting for information about whether the client has a second insurance plan covering him or her.

Place-of-service code: See POS code

Plan: An employee benefits arrangement offered by an insurance company so that health care services are provided to covered members or enrollees in the plan.

Point-of-service plan: See POS plan.

Policyholder: The individual to whom an insurance contract is issued, usually the employee in an employer-sponsored health plan. Also called the subscriber.

Portability: The ability for an individual to transfer from one health insurance plan to another (including after a change of job status, or change of plans offered by the employer) and still be covered.

POS (Place-of-service) code: This code, placed on a claim form, informs insurance companies where the treatment took place.

POS (point-of-service) plan: A health plan allowing members to choose to receive services from participating or non-participating providers. Some plans afford clients the choice to see the plan's HMO providers, PPO providers, or any licensed provider, and their coverage level will vary accordingly. If the client chooses an out-of-network provider, out-of-pocket expenses may be higher.

PPO (preferred provider organization): A managed care health plan with a network of providers. The health plan has contracted with these providers to provide services at a discounted fee. Clients can visit providers both in and out of the network, but will pay a higher portion of the cost for an out-of-network provider. Network providers must file claims on the client's behalf. Members don't need to choose a primary care physician for coverage, and can visit specialists without a referral.

Pre-authorization: The process of obtaining approval from the health plan for sessions or hospital admission prior to the start of treatment.

Pre-certification: See Pre-authorization.

Pre-existing condition: A health condition (other than pregnancy) that was diagnosed or treated within six months prior to the client's enrollment in a new health plan (or a condition for which a reasonable person would have sought medical advice). Prior to the Affordable Care Act, many insurance plans would not cover pre-existing conditions, or would only cover them after a waiting period. Plans that still can exclude pre-existing conditions are rare.

Preferred provider organization plan: See PPO

Premium: The upfront amount the client or employer pays monthly or yearly in exchange for health insurance coverage.

Primary care physician (PCP): A client's main physician, usually a family or general practitioner, internist (or for children, pediatrician), who provides a broad range of routine medical services and refers clients to specialists, hospitals, and other providers as needed. Some health plans require that the client has a PCP, and may require a PCP's referral to obtain services from other providers.

Prior authorization: See Pre-authorization.

Private-pay Agreement: An agreement between client and therapist where the client agrees to pay for services out of pocket (see sample on Page 149).

Provider: A licensed health care facility, program, agency, physician, or other health professional that delivers health care services.

Provider network: A panel of providers contracted by a health plan to deliver medical services to the enrollees. The providers usually agree to accept a fee discount, and to file claims on behalf of the client. Also called a provider panel.

Provider panel: See Provider network

Quality assurance: The steps taken by a managed care health plan to ensure quality of care, including provider credentialing, auditing, treatment reviews, and other monitoring of provider care.

Recredentialing: A process used by a managed care company in which a network provider's information is updated and credentials are again reviewed and matched against the qualifications required to participate in the provider network. This is done at regular intervals (ex. every 1-3 years).

Retro-authorization: An authorization for treatment given by an insurance company after the date of service has already passed.

SED (serious emotional disturbance): In certain state parity laws, children are afforded mental health coverage which is equal to that of medical coverage if they have diagnoses which meet the criteria in the state's parity law for "serious emotional disturbance."

Self-funded/self-insured plan: This is a type of health plan that is self-funded by the employer. Some plans contract with insurance carriers for claims processing and other administrative services, others may be self-administered. With self-funded plans, federal law (instead of state law) applies, and the benefits may be different from non-self-funded insurance plans.

Serious Emotional Disturbance: See SED

Severe mental illness (SMI): This term is used in some state parity laws. In these state laws, only clients with a diagnosis that qualifies as a "severe mental illness" may be entitled to coverage that is equal to the coverage the plan offers for medical claims. Also known as "parity diagnoses."

Single case agreement: When an appropriate provider cannot be found who is available to provide services within a reasonable distance from the client and within the client's provider network, or when no network providers have the specialized training or expertise a client needs, a health plan may often be compelled to contract with an out of network provider to act as a network provider for this one case. Also known as an ad hoc agreement. See also "transition of care agreements."

SMI : See Severe mental illness.

Split-year claims: Claims that have charges from two or more years on the form (not recommended).

Subscriber: The holder of the insurance – the primary insured person who is enrolled and eligible for coverage under a health plan.

Superbill: A list of charges and payments made for healthcare services provided. This may be given to a client to submit to their insurance plan for reimbursement. Also known as a statement or invoice.

Telehealth: Providing treatment, education, and administration of health services over a distance. While each state defines telehealth differently, it typically involves the application of both video and audio technologies in synchronous treatment delivery (some states include telephone in their definition).

Third-party administrator (TPA): An individual or firm hired by the employer to handle claims processing, pay providers, and manage other functions related to health insurance.

Third-party payer: Any payer for health care services other than the client. Examples include insurance companies and the federal government.

Transitional benefits/plans: When an employer changes insurance carriers, transition plans enable clients already in treatment to transition to a provider in the new network. They give the client and his current provider a specific number of days to contact the insurance company in order to discuss the client's treatment plan and to obtain authorization to continue treatment at the network benefit level for a specified period of time, or to transition to a professional in the new network.

TRICARE: The Defense Department's managed care plan for military dependents and retirees.

Usual, customary and reasonable (UCR) charges: The amount that the insurance company has determined is reasonable for a particular service, taking into account the providers degree, licensure, and the usual fees for similar providers in your geographical area. The UCR is the maximum the plan will pay for any service. Since network providers have contracted rates, this applies only to out-of-network providers.

Utilization: Measurement of the use of health insurance by employees of an insured employer, stated in terms of the average number of claims per employee.

Utilization management/review (UM/UR): The processes by which an insurance plan reviews a provider's treatment requests to determine whether care decisions are appropriate and to make reimbursement decisions, with a view to contain costs and monitor quality of care. This review may take place before, during, or after services have been rendered.

Sample Treatment Agreement

FEES: The fee per 50-minute session is $_____ (except for the first session, which is $_____). This is payable at the time of our session, unless I am billing your insurance, in which case you must pay your copayment and/or deductible at the session.

CANCELLATION: You may be charged $_____ (not just a copayment) for sessions missed or cancelled without 24-hour notice, except in medical emergency. <u>Insurance will not pay for missed sessions.</u>

INSURANCE: If I am a provider with your plan, I will submit claims for you, but at our session you must pay any portion not covered by your plan. If I am <u>NOT</u> a provider for your plan, you will pay me in full at the session, and I can give you an invoice so that you can seek reimbursement from your plan.

PLEASE SIGN IF USING YOUR INSURANCE OR EMPLOYEE ASSISTANCE PROGRAM:

"I authorize the release of any information necessary (including notes, treatment summaries and diagnosis) to my insurance plan or EAP to process claims, determine medical necessity, or to request additional sessions."

(Sign here) :**X** _____

(If applicable, second client sign here): _____

"I authorize payment of benefits to my provider." (Sign here): **X** _____

CONFIDENTIALITY: What you say in therapy, your records, and your attendance are all confidential. Exceptions include when your records are subpoenaed for legal reasons, when reporting is required or allowed by law (ex. suspected child/elder abuse or neglect, extreme danger to self, or danger to others), when you sign a release, and other exceptions outlined in my *Notice of Privacy Practices.*

EMERGENCY: Leave a message on my voicemail, then call my answering service at _____ (they will try to reach me or another licensed therapist) or go to the emergency room or dial 911.

ENDINGS: You may end therapy at any time, but a final phone call or session is requested for closure. It is my ethical duty to provide therapy only when your issues are within the scope of my training, when I feel you are actively participating in treatment, and when I feel you are benefiting from the sessions.

E-MAIL: I do not do therapy by e-mail or Skype. I prefer to use e-mail only to arrange appointments. When cancelling a session, please leave BOTH voicemail and e-mail messages. Please do not e-mail me information related to your therapy, as it is not completely confidential. Be aware that e-mails between us become part of your legal record.

SOCIAL MEDIA: I do not accept "friend requests" or contact requests from current or former clients on social networking sites (Facebook, LinkedIn, etc) out of concern for your confidentiality and my privacy. It may also blur the boundaries of the therapy relationship.

DISCLAIMER: I am not responsible for care received from professionals I refer you to. Our agreements do not involve other providers in the suite, who operate solo independent practices (we are not a group).

PRIVACY POLICY: By signing below, you acknowledge receipt of my *Notices of Privacy Practices.* My *Notice* provides information about how I may use and disclose your private health information. I encourage you to read it in full. My *Notice of Privacy* Practices is subject to change. If I change my Notice, I will give you a revised Notice. If you have left treatment, you may obtain the revised notice from me at the above address. If you have questions about the Notice or any of the above, feel free to ask.

X_____ **X**_____ _____
Signature   Printed Name   Date

X_____ **X**_____ _____
Signature, second client, if applicable   Printed Name, second client   Date

APPENDIX E
Sample Invoice/Superbill

BARBARA GRISWOLD, MFT
LICENSED MARRIAGE & FAMILY THERAPIST
4100 MOORPARK AVE. #116, SAN JOSE, CA 95117
TEL 408-985-0846   EMAIL BARBGRIS@AOL.COM

INVOICE DATE:_____/_____/_____

Client:	Birthdate: / /
SSN or Plan ID:	Group # :

DIAGNOSIS CODE(S):_____

Date	Place of Service Code	CPT Code	Service Description, Activity or Payment Type	Charges	Credits

Make Payment To:
☐ Client: _____
☐ Barbara Griswold, LMFT
☐ Other: _____

Previous Balance	$
New Charges	$
New Credits	$
Total Owed	$
Date Due	

_____
SIGNATURE: BARBARA GRISWOLD, MFT (MFC27210)
TAX ID: XXX-XX-XXXX
NPI: XXXXXXXXXX

145

APPENDIX F

Sample Service Record

Client Name: Jack Klutz		Diagnosis: 309.81, 305.20							Copay: $15.00	
Sessions Authorized: 8 Start: 7/1/14 Expires:7/1/15 Auth#: 1005678							Contract rate: $75 intake/couples; ind $65			
Sessions Authorized: ___ Start: _____ Expires: _____ Auth#: _____							Deduct: $500 Used? $500			
Sessions Authorized: ___ Start: _____ Expires: _____ Auth#: _____										

Service Date	Ses #	Client Seen	Service Description	Fee Charged (may be Contract rate)	Payment Made	Ct. Copay Owed	Ct. Owes Total	Ins. Owes For Ses.	Ins. Owes Total	Did Ins. Pay?
7/1/2014	1 of 8	Jack	Intake Ses.	$75.00	$15.00	$15.00	$0.00	$60.00	$60.00	√
7/8/2014	2 of 8	Jack	Individual Ses.	$65.00	$15.00	$15.00	$0.00	$50.00	$110.00	√
7/20/2014	3 of 8	Jack & Jill	Couples Ses.	$75.00	$15.00	$15.00	$0.00	$60.00	$170.00	√
7/30/2014	4 of 8	Jack	Individual Ses.	$65.00	$15.00	$15.00	$0.00	$50.00	$220.00	√
8/1/2014	—	—	Bill Ins 7/2014	—	—	—	$0.00	—	$220.00	—
9/7/2014	—	—	Ins. Pd. 7/2014	—	$220.00	—	$0.00	—	$0.00	—

APPENDIX G

Sample Private Pay Agreement
ೞ ೞ

I, _____ (client name), by signing this agreement, indicate that I understand that my treatment with _____ (provider name) beginning _____ (date), will not be covered by insurance because:

_____ I attest that I do not have insurance coverage for the services I am seeking

_____ I am choosing not to use my insurance coverage for my treatment. In doing so, I understand that I may not get the benefit of any provider discounts, and that my provider is not obligated to bill the plan. I understand that in doing so I waive any future right to bill insurance or be reimbursed by an insurance plan for sessions that have already taken place

_____ I have been notified by my provider or by my insurance plan that my treatment will not be covered by my health plan because:

    _____ It is not (or no longer) a covered benefit under my insurance plan

    _____ It is not (or no longer) covered because the plan has determined the treatment does not meet the plan's standards for medical necessity

    _____ I desire more frequent or longer services than are covered by my plan

_____ Other:_____

_____

If this is the result of a decision by my health plan, I have been informed about the reason, am aware of my plan's formal appeal process, have elected not to appeal, or am in the process of appealing. In the meantime/instead I elect to continue therapy on an out-of-pocket basis, and I understand I will not be reimbursed by my insurance unless I am successful on appeal.

I agree that the provider may collect charges for the services at his/her full fee-for-service rate, or at the rates outlined below. I understand that insurance plan maximums will not apply and will not limit the amount I may become obligated to pay for the proposed services.

$_____(amount) for _____ (type of services)
$_____(amount) for _____ (type of services)
$_____(amount) for _____ (type of services)

I understand that I have a right to a copy of this form. This consent is subject to revocation at any time except to the extent that action has been already taken in reliance thereon. By signing this agreement, I am creating a binding contract that is legally enforceable against me by the provider.

_____   _____
Client signature (or responsible party)   Date

_____   _____
Therapist signature   Date

149

Index